MAKING
READING
CONNECTIONS

Book D

CURRICULUM ASSOCIATES®, Inc.

ISBN 0-7609-2076-1
©2003—Curriculum Associates, Inc.
North Billerica, MA 01862

15 14 13 12 11 10 9 8 7 6 5 4 3

Table of Contents

1 Finding Main Idea

PART ONE: Learn About Main Idea

Read this paragraph about the Grand Canyon in northwest Arizona. The first sentence of the paragraph is underlined. This sentence tells the most important idea in the paragraph.

Paintbox Rocks

<u>The Grand Canyon is a grand display of changing colors.</u> Like all canyons, the Grand Canyon is a deep valley formed by a river. The walls of the Grand Canyon are made up of many layers of different shades of rock. Some layers are

pink, red, or green. Some layers are purple, orange, or even blue. As the sun rises, the colors shift from dim and dark to bright and vivid. At noontime, the reds and greens seem to disappear. At sunset, the reds and oranges glow for awhile before all the colors blend to a misty gray.

The paragraph is about the Grand Canyon.
The first sentence of the paragraph states the most important idea about the Grand Canyon.
The Grand Canyon is a grand display of changing colors.

The most important idea in a paragraph is called the **main idea**.
The main idea tells what a paragraph is mostly about.

▶ The main idea is sometimes found in the first sentence of the paragraph.

▶ The main idea is sometimes found in the last sentence of the paragraph.

▶ The main idea is sometimes not found in any one sentence. You can figure out the main idea on your own. Think about what you have read. Then ask yourself, "What is the most important idea in the paragraph?" Your answer to this question will help you figure out the main idea.

Read this paragraph about a kind of insect. As you read, think about the most important idea in the paragraph. Then answer the questions.

Cooperating Insects

Most insects live alone. They do not spend time together or work with others of their kind. But a few types of insects live a different kind of life. One of these insects is the honeybee. Honeybees live together in a colony. In the colony, each bee has one of three main jobs. Workers build the nests. They gather pollen and nectar from the flowers. They use pollen for food. Workers change the nectar to honey to feed the grubs, or young bees. The queen bee, one per nest, lays the eggs that hatch into grubs. Drones mate with the queen bee. Insects like honeybees work cooperatively to help the group grow larger and stay strong.

1. What is the main idea of the paragraph?

   Ⓐ Most insects live alone.
   Ⓑ Workers build the nests, gather pollen, make honey, and feed the grubs.
   Ⓒ Each bee in a colony has one of three main jobs.
   Ⓓ Insects like honeybees work cooperatively to help the group grow larger and stay strong.

2. Where or how did you find the main idea?

   Ⓐ in the first sentence of the paragraph
   Ⓑ in the second sentence of the paragraph
   Ⓒ in the last sentence of the paragraph
   Ⓓ by thinking about the most important idea in the paragraph

Work with a partner. Talk about your answers to questions 1 and 2. Tell why you chose the answers you did.

PART TWO: Check Your Understanding

Remember: The main idea tells what a paragraph is mostly about.

▸ Read the first sentence of the paragraph. The main idea of the paragraph is sometimes found here.

▸ Read the last sentence of the paragraph. The main idea of the paragraph is sometimes found here.

▸ Sometimes, the main idea is not found in any one sentence. You can figure out the main idea by thinking about the most important idea in the paragraph. Ask yourself, "What is the paragraph mostly about?"

Read this paragraph about Alexander Graham Bell. As you read, ask yourself, "What is the paragraph mostly about?" Then answer the questions.

Alexander Graham Bell was clever. When he was young, he had learned to teach children who could not hear or speak. This made him think of the different ways that people communicate. Bell kept these ideas about communication in his head. He thought about their importance. He came to believe he could invent a special machine. This machine would let a person talk to someone who was far away. After three years of hard work with Thomas Watson, Bell tested his invention. In 1876, he spoke the first words into a working telephone. Watson heard him in the next room.

3. What is the paragraph mostly about?
   Ⓐ Bell worked for three years with Thomas Watson.
   Ⓑ Bell tested his invention in 1876.
   Ⓒ Bell used his ideas about communication to invent the telephone.
   Ⓓ Watson did not hear Bell speak in the next room.

4. Where or how did you find the main idea?
   Ⓐ in the first sentence of the paragraph
   Ⓑ in the second sentence of the paragraph
   Ⓒ in the last sentence of the paragraph
   Ⓓ by thinking about the most important idea in the paragraph

Look at the answer choices for each question.
Read why each answer choice is correct or not correct.

3. What is the paragraph mostly about?

   Ⓐ Bell worked for three years with Thomas Watson.

   This answer is not correct because it tells one detail about Bell. This is only one idea in the paragraph. It is not the most important idea.

   Ⓑ Bell tested his invention in 1876.

   This answer is not correct because it tells about only one of the things Bell did. This is only one idea in the paragraph. The paragraph is not mostly about Bell speaking the first words into the telephone.

   ● Bell used his ideas about communication to invent the telephone.

   This answer is correct because it tells what all the sentences in the paragraph are mostly about. It is the most important idea of the paragraph.

   Ⓓ Watson did not hear Bell speak in the next room.

   This answer is not correct because it tells a detail that is not true according to the paragraph. Even if this detail was true, it would not be the most important idea of the paragraph.

4. Where or how did you find the main idea?

   Ⓐ in the first sentence of the paragraph

   This answer is not correct because the first sentence is "Alexander Graham Bell was clever." This describes Bell, but it is not the most important idea of the paragraph.

   Ⓑ in the second sentence of the paragraph

   This answer is not correct because the second sentence of the paragraph tells about what Bell did when he was young. This is not what the paragraph is mostly about. Also, the main idea is more often found in the first or last sentence of a paragraph, not the second.

   Ⓒ in the last sentence of the paragraph

   This answer is not correct because the last sentence is "Watson heard him in the next room." This is not the most important idea of the paragraph.

   ● by thinking about the most important idea in the paragraph

   This answer is correct because the main idea is not found in the first sentence, the second sentence, or the last sentence of the paragraph. The main idea is found by thinking about all of the sentences in the paragraph and deciding what they are mostly about.

PART THREE: Learn More About Main Idea

▶ Each paragraph in a reading passage has one main idea.

▶ All the paragraphs together in a reading passage also have one main idea. The main idea of a reading passage with two or more paragraphs is sometimes found in the first paragraph or the last paragraph.

▶ The title of a reading passage often gives a clue to the main idea of the whole passage. If no title is given, think of a title on your own. Ask yourself, "What would be a good title for this reading passage?" Your answer to this question will help you figure out the main idea.

Read this report about rain forests. As you read, think about the main idea of each paragraph. Also think about the main idea of the whole report. Then answer the questions.

Disappearing Jewels

Rain forests around the world are being destroyed at an alarming rate. A rain forest can change from a place of lush trees to a barren desert in fewer than ten years. This is because the soil in a rain forest is poor and thin. The roots of the tall trees are all that hold the soil in place. Without the trees, the soil washes away and the rain forest dies.

Farmers are one cause of the loss of these natural jewels. Farmers cut down trees to clear land for planting. But in a few years, the soil is washed away and no plants grow. Farmers must clear more land, continuing the destruction.

Loggers, who cut trees for lumber, also put rain forests at risk. Rain falls, carrying the soil away into rivers and streams. The land stays empty of life. The jewel of a forest is gone.

5. What is the main idea of the first paragraph?
   Ⓐ Rain forest soil is poor and thin.
   Ⓑ Rain forest trees have long roots.
   Ⓒ Rain forests are disappearing.
   Ⓓ Rain forests are like deserts.

6. What is the main idea of the last paragraph?
   Ⓐ Loggers put rain forests at risk.
   Ⓑ Lots of rain falls in a rain forest.
   Ⓒ Farming destroys rain forests.
   Ⓓ Soil can wash into rivers.

7. What is the report mostly about?
   Ⓐ the destruction of rain forests
   Ⓑ farmers who plant in rain forests
   Ⓒ people who cut lumber
   Ⓓ the poor soil of rain forests

8. Which is another good title for the report?
   Ⓐ "Farming the Rain Forests"
   Ⓑ "Losing Our Precious Rain Forests"
   Ⓒ "The Treasure of Good Lumber"
   Ⓓ "Rain Forest Trees"

Read this folktale about songbirds. Then answer the questions.

Long ago, the sun disappeared behind some dark clouds that refused to budge. Day after day, the forest songbirds lived in darkness. Without the sunlight, the songbirds could not do the one thing they loved most, which was to sing.

Desperate, the songbirds called a meeting to discuss the problem. They all agreed that something must be done, but they did not feel clever enough to find a solution. Someone suggested that they ask Mr. Owl to help them. So they did. But Mr. Owl did not wish to solve the problem. He rather liked the darkness, both day and night. Someone else suggested that the songbirds ask Miss Hawk to help them. So they did. But Miss Hawk claimed the darkness helped her hunt without being seen.

Finally, the songbirds decided to solve the problem themselves. A group of 20 songbirds volunteered to fly into the clouds, flap their wings, and screech. When they did this, the clouds broke up and ran away. All the songbirds sang joyfully as rays of bright sunlight lit the forest. The songbirds had found a way to solve their problem all by themselves.

9. What is the main idea of paragraph two?

   Ⓐ Mr. Owl prefers darkness to sunlight.
   Ⓑ The songbirds ask others to help them solve a problem.
   Ⓒ Miss Hawk can hunt better when there is less light.
   Ⓓ The songbirds think of a clever idea.

10. The last paragraph is mostly about

    Ⓐ how the songbirds solved their own problem.
    Ⓑ why the songbirds were joyful.
    Ⓒ how the songbirds convinced other birds to solve their problem.
    Ⓓ why the clouds had appeared in the sky.

11. What is the main message of the folktale?

    Ⓐ Some songbirds can fly very high.
    Ⓑ We are often better able to solve our problems than we think we are.
    Ⓒ Always try to get someone to solve your problems for you.
    Ⓓ You should never ask for help with a problem.

12. Which of these is the best title for the folktale?

    Ⓐ "Finding Your Own Way"
    Ⓑ "Flying to the Sun"
    Ⓒ "Helping the Hawks and Owls"
    Ⓓ "The Cloudy Day"

PART FOUR: Prepare for a Test

▶ A test question about the main idea may ask you what a reading passage is *mostly* or *mainly* about.

▶ A test question about the main idea may ask you to choose the best title for the reading passage. The best title is the one that tells the main idea of the whole passage.

Here is a story about a boy named Max. Read the story. Then do Numbers 13 and 14.

Max dropped his schoolbooks inside the door of his apartment and grabbed his basketball from the hall closet. He had gotten home early. He wanted to practice shooting baskets just like he did every day. He headed to the basketball court at the lot across the street. No one was around. Calm and relaxed, Max dribbled, set up, and shot, making basket after basket. He felt great when the ball dropped into the net time after time.

Suddenly, Max noticed Johan and Jim, two older boys who were on the basketball team that Max wanted to join. Max wanted to impress them. But now he felt tense. He dribbled, set up, and lifted his arms gracefully for a clear shot. The ball bumped the rim of the basket and flew back into his grasp. He shot again, and this time the ball skirted around the rim, but dropped outside the edge. A third attempt failed as well. Max knew he would need to gain more confidence to make the basketball team.

Finding Main Idea

13. The story is mostly about a boy who
   Ⓐ wants to get on a basketball team.
   Ⓑ won't shoot baskets when people are watching.
   Ⓒ loves basketball more than school.
   Ⓓ feels lonely.

Finding Main Idea

14. The best title for the story is
   Ⓐ "Max's Perfect Shots."
   Ⓑ "After-School Sports."
   Ⓒ "A Team Sport."
   Ⓓ "Max's Need for Nerve."

Here is an article about a different kind of worker. Read the article. Then do Numbers 15 and 16.

In the 1950s, a new kind of worker showed up in the workplace. This worker didn't need time for lunch and other breaks. The worker was never late for work and never had to leave early. This worker never smiled or talked. This worker was a robot.

Today, robots are used in car factories to build cars. The sheet metal and car parts are loaded onto an assembly line. Then the robots take over. They do work that humans would find boring. A robot may attach a bolt onto the same type of car part over 300 times in one hour.

Food manufacturers also use robot workers. The robots make plastic food containers. They wrap ice-cream bars and package raisins.

Robots are often used to do jobs that are dangerous. Robots can safely heat metal parts that need to be welded, or joined together. They can also handle harmful chemicals without risk of injury.

Robots working at a car assembly plant

Finding Main Idea

15. The article is mostly about
    ⓐ why robots are used in food factories.
    ⓑ how robots can be useful in the workplace.
    ⓒ why robots are better workers than humans.
    ⓓ how robots bolt on the same part over and over.

Finding Main Idea

16. Which of these is the best title for the article?
    ⓐ "Robot Workers"
    ⓑ "The Life of a Robot"
    ⓒ "Harmful Chemicals"
    ⓓ "The Automobile Factory"

Recalling Facts and Details

PART ONE: Learn About Facts and Details

> Read this paragraph about strange creatures. The main idea is stated in the first sentence. The main idea sentence is underlined for you. As you read, think about the sentences that tell more about the main idea.

<u>In many lakes around the world, people claim to have seen strange creatures.</u> The creatures are said to have the body of a serpent and the head of a horse. Nessie is the lake monster believed to live in Loch Ness, Scotland. Champ is a creature that some say lives in Lake Champlain, New York. Similar sightings have been made in Turkey, Canada, and Norway. No one knows if these lake monsters are real. The search for answers, however, will continue for years to come.

The sentences that tell more about the main idea are
The creatures are said to have the body of a serpent and the head of a horse.
Nessie is the lake monster believed to live in Loch Ness, Scotland.
Champ is a creature that some say lives in Lake Champlain, New York.
Similar sightings have been made in Turkey, Canada, and Norway.
No one knows if these lake monsters are real.
The search for answers, however, will continue for years to come.

Sentences that tell more about the main idea are called **facts and details**. Facts and details explain or support the most important idea in a paragraph.

▮▷ Facts and details provide information about the main idea.

▮▷ Facts and details often tell *who, what, where, when, why,* and *how* about the main idea.

Read this paragraph about Emma. The main idea is found in the last sentence. It is underlined for you. As you read, think about the facts and details that tell more about the main idea. Then answer the questions.

The Collector

Whenever we go to the beach, Emma wanders along the shore picking up patterned shells. She keeps the ones she likes best to put away in her box of shells. When we hike through the woods in the fall, Emma gathers the brightest leaves to paste in her leaf album. At the lake, Emma looks for the shiniest stones. She takes them home to set on a shelf. She prefers the round polished stones that are pure white or golden yellow. <u>Emma is always collecting things from nature</u>.

1. What does Emma collect when she hikes?

Ⓐ leaves
Ⓑ shells
Ⓒ flowers
Ⓓ stones

2. Which detail tells what Emma does with the items she collects from the lake?

Ⓐ She puts them in an album.
Ⓑ She places them on a shelf.
Ⓒ She puts them in a box.
Ⓓ She polishes them to make them shiny.

Work with a partner. Talk about your answers to questions 1 and 2. Tell why you chose the answers you did.

PART TWO: Check Your Understanding

Remember: Facts and details explain or support the main idea.

▶ Look for sentences that provide information about the main idea.

▶ Look for sentences that explain *who, what, where, when, why,* and *how* about the main idea.

Read this article about early ballpoint pens. As you read, ask yourself, "What is the main idea? What facts and details tell *more* about the main idea?" Then answer the questions.

The Ballpoint Pen's First Failures

During the mid-1900s, several inventors came up with the idea of a ballpoint pen. The first pens of this type were sold in the United States in 1945.

Purchasers of these new pens were in for big surprises. The ink inside the pen often came out in lumps. Sometimes air bubbles blocked the flow of ink. The pen would no longer write. When the pen did write, another surprise awaited the owner. The ink often faded. The writing sometimes disappeared! This caused annoying problems for letter writers and record keepers. Bankers were the most horrified. Checks and important records could go blank without warning. The ballpoint pen needed more work!

3. Which of these was <u>not</u> a problem with the first ballpoint pens?

   Ⓐ Sometimes the pen did not write.

   Ⓑ Sometimes the ink came out in lumps.

   Ⓒ Sometimes the pen tore through paper.

   Ⓓ Sometimes the ink faded.

4. According to the article, who was most upset about the disappearing ink?

   Ⓐ letter writers

   Ⓑ inventors

   Ⓒ record keepers

   Ⓓ bankers

**Look at the answer choices for each question.
Read why each answer choice is correct or not correct.**

3. Which of these was <u>not</u> a problem with the first ballpoint pens?

Ⓐ Sometimes the pen did not write.

This answer is not correct because the second paragraph says, "Sometimes air bubbles blocked the flow of ink. The pen would no longer write." So, the pen not writing was a problem with the first ballpoint pen.

Ⓑ Sometimes the ink came out in lumps.

This answer is not correct because the second paragraph says, "The ink inside the pen often came out in lumps." So, ink coming out in lumps was a problem with the first ballpoint pen.

● Sometimes the pen tore through paper.

This answer is correct because none of the paragraphs in the article tell about the pen tearing through paper.

Ⓓ Sometimes the ink faded.

This answer is not correct because the second paragraph says, "The ink often faded." So, ink fading was a problem with the first ballpoint pen.

4. According to the article, who was most upset about the disappearing ink?

Ⓐ letter writers

This answer is not correct because the second paragraph tells how disappearing ink was an annoying problem for letter writers and record keepers. Nothing in the paragraph tells that either of them was the most upset about this annoyance.

Ⓑ inventors

This answer is not correct because there is no information in the article that reveals how inventors felt about any of the problems with the ballpoint pen, including how they felt about the disappearing ink.

Ⓒ record keepers

This answer is not correct because the second paragraph tells how disappearing ink was an annoying problem for letter writers and record keepers. Nothing in the paragraph tells that either of them was the most upset about this annoyance.

● bankers

This answer is correct because the second paragraph says, "Bankers were the most horrified." This tells you that bankers were the most upset about the disappearing ink.

PART THREE: Learn More About Facts and Details

Writers use facts and details for many reasons. Facts and details can

▶ describe a person, a place, or a thing.

▶ explain how to do something.

▶ tell the order in which things happen.

▶ share an experience, an idea, or an opinion.

> Read this article about a famous comic strip. Then answer the questions.

You're a Good Man, Charlie Brown

Charles M. Schulz created one of the most popular comic strips of all time. He chose to call it *Li'l Folks*. United Features, the publisher of the comic strip, changed the title to *Peanuts*.

The comic strip was first published on October 2, 1950. It appeared in only seven newspapers. People liked the characters Schulz created. One was Charlie Brown. He always seemed to fail. Charlie's dog Snoopy was funny. Bossy Lucy made people laugh.

Over time, more readers loved the comic strip. By the mid-1990s, more than 2,000 papers printed the comic strip weekly. It was translated into two dozen languages. Today, the characters are still found in books, movies, and TV specials. There is even a stage play about them called *You're a Good Man, Charlie Brown*.

5. Schulz's comic strip was first published in
   Ⓐ 1950.
   Ⓑ October 1902.
   Ⓒ the mid-1990s.
   Ⓓ 2000.

6. Which of these is a fact about Charles Schulz?
   Ⓐ He always seemed to fail.
   Ⓑ He had a stage play written about him.
   Ⓒ He created a popular comic strip.
   Ⓓ He translated his work into two dozen languages.

7. What is the name of the comic strip?
   Ⓐ *You're a Good Man, Charlie Brown*
   Ⓑ *Li'l Folks*
   Ⓒ *Peanuts*
   Ⓓ *Snoopy*

8. Which detail tells more about the main idea of paragraph three?
   Ⓐ The bossy character Lucy made people laugh.
   Ⓑ The comic strip was translated into two dozen languages.
   Ⓒ Over time, more readers loved the comic strip.
   Ⓓ Charlie Brown's dog Snoopy was funny.

Read this Viking legend. Then answer the questions.

A statue of Thor

Thor, thunder god of the Vikings, had lost his hammer. His hammer was the only weapon that could kill the evil giants who threatened his people. Loki, a god who played tricks, turned himself into a falcon. He searched for the missing hammer.

Loki learned that a giant named Thrym had stolen the hammer and buried it. Thrym would not say where. And he would not return the hammer unless the goddess Freyja married him. Freyja refused. So a wise man told Thor to dress up as Freyja, with a full bridal veil.

Thor's hammer

Loki led the disguised Thor to the land of the giants. The giants were pleased to see Freyja. But her behavior shocked them. She ate enough for ten men. Her eyes shone red beneath the veil.

Loki explained that Freyja had not eaten or slept for eight days. She was too excited about the wedding. The giants believed Loki. Thrym placed the hammer on the lap of his bride. Thor jumped from behind the veil and grabbed his hammer. With the hammer, Thor and Loki returned safely home.

A statue of Freyja

9. What is one detail about Loki?

Ⓐ He can eat enough for ten men.

Ⓑ He can turn into a falcon.

Ⓒ He owns an important hammer.

Ⓓ He is the thunder god.

10. Which detail tells about the main idea of the first paragraph?

Ⓐ A giant wanted to marry Freyja.

Ⓑ Thor hid under a veil.

Ⓒ Thor's hammer could kill evil giants.

Ⓓ Thor had not eaten or slept for eight days.

11. Who was Thrym?

Ⓐ an evil giant

Ⓑ the thunder god

Ⓒ a Viking goddess

Ⓓ a god who can play tricks

12. Which of these tells more about the main idea of the last paragraph?

Ⓐ Thor grabbed the hammer.

Ⓑ Freyja refused to marry Thrym.

Ⓒ Thor was afraid of Thrym.

Ⓓ Loki led Thor to the land of the giants.

PART FOUR: Prepare for a Test

▣ A test question about facts and details may ask you for something that is stated in a reading passage.

▣ A test question about facts and details may ask you *who, what, where, when, why,* and *how* about the main idea.

Here is an article about nuts people eat. Read the article.
Then do Numbers 13 and 14.

Nuts to You!

A nut is a seed or fruit that has a woody shell. Hundreds of types of trees and bushes produce nuts.

Three common nuts grown for food are almonds, walnuts, and pecans. Of these three kinds of nuts, almonds are the most common. About 80% of the world's almonds are grown in California. The largest almond factory is also located there. The factory packages two million pounds of almonds a day.

English walnuts are the next most common kind of nut. They are also called Persian walnuts. About 66% of the walnuts in the world come from California.

Pecans are raised in many places. Most pecans are grown in the United States and Mexico. A smaller number are grown in Australia, South Africa, and the Middle East.

Upper left, pecans; upper right, walnuts; bottom, almonds

Recalling Facts and Details

13. What two types of nuts are grown mostly in California?

   Ⓐ almonds and English walnuts
   Ⓑ English walnuts and pecans
   Ⓒ almonds and pecans
   Ⓓ Persian walnuts and pecans

Recalling Facts and Details

14. A factory in California packages
   Ⓐ all of the world's almonds.
   Ⓑ 66% of the world's pecans.
   Ⓒ two million pounds of almonds every day.
   Ⓓ pecans.

Here is a story about a hiking adventure. Read the story.
Then do Numbers 15 and 16.

Erik followed the trail that led through Hovenweep National Monument.
He hiked carefully along the rim of a deep valley that was green with trees.
The ranger had told him not to leave the trail. Snakes and other wild animals
lurked in the brush.

All around, Erik could see the ancient ruins of Indian villages. The Anasazi
had built these homes of stone in the 1200s. They had lived here for a hundred
years before a drought struck. They moved away. The Ute Indians named the
village *Hovenweep*, or "Deserted Valley."

Among the ruins, the air blew fresh and cool. Erik hiked past the crumbling
walls and towers. He edged along the rim until a rustling in the brush on the side
of the trail startled him. Was it a lizard, like the ones he had seen scurrying here
and there all day?

Suddenly, the rustling changed to rattling.
Right in front of Erik was a small rattlesnake.
Erik froze. Slowly, the rattler eased across the path
and into the brush on the other side. "The ranger
never said the *path* wasn't safe," Erik sighed as
he hiked on, listening carefully for every sound.

Recalling Facts and Details

15. Who named the ruins *Hovenweep*?

Ⓐ the Anasazi Indians

Ⓑ the ranger

Ⓒ the hiker

Ⓓ the Ute Indians

Recalling Facts and Details

16. What is one fact about
the ancient ruins?

Ⓐ They are deep in a valley.

Ⓑ They were discovered in the last
one hundred years.

Ⓒ Anasazi Indians built them
in the 1200s.

Ⓓ The Ute Indians lived there
in about 1300.

3 Understanding Sequence

PART ONE: Learn About Sequence

Read these instructions for making a paper airplane. As you read, think about the order of the steps needed to make the airplane. The underlined words give clues to the order in which things are done.

An Airplane That Flies!

Making a paper airplane that really flies is easy. <u>First</u>, take an $8\frac{1}{2}$ by 11-inch sheet of paper and fold it the long way. Hold the paper with the fold down. <u>Second</u>, fold each left-hand corner diagonally down to the main fold. The piece you are folding will look like a triangle. <u>Third</u>, fold each top edge down to meet the main fold. Now the airplane looks sleek. <u>Fourth</u>, fold over the point, or nose of the plane, about $\frac{1}{2}$ inch. This makes the airplane heavier in front. <u>Finally</u>, thrust your plane into the air and give it a fly!

The order of the steps needed to make a paper airplane is:
First, take an $8\frac{1}{2}$ by 11-inch sheet of paper and fold it the long way.
Second, fold each left-hand corner diagonally down to the main fold.
Third, fold each top edge down to meet the main fold.
Fourth, fold over the point, or nose of the plane, about $\frac{1}{2}$ inch.
Finally, thrust your plane into the air and give it a fly!

The order in which things are done or events happen is called **sequence**. The steps for completing a set of directions often follow a sequence.

- Clue words such as *first, next, then, last, finally, before,* and *after* often tell you when things are done or events happen.

- Clues such as times of day, days of the week, months, seasons, and years tell when things happen.

- Sometimes, there are no clue words. In a story, think about the beginning, the middle, and the ending to help you figure out the sequence. In an article, think about the order in which things happen or how things are done.

Read this description of Lara's drama class. As you read, think about what happens first, second, and so on. Then answer the questions.

Drama Class

Drama class is the only class this year that is broken into parts. In the first part of the class, we listen to the drama teacher tell us about a drama topic. Yesterday, we learned about the stage. Today, we will study stage directions. Next, during the second part of class, we will work in groups and write a skit. The skits we write are usually about something simple. For example, one of us might be a customer in a pet store and another might be the clerk. One of us might even be the cute dog that the customer wants to buy. During the last part of class, we will act out our skit. That is the best part of class for me.

1. What do the students do in the first part of drama class?

   Ⓐ They act out a skit.
   Ⓑ They write a skit.
   Ⓒ They listen to the teacher.
   Ⓓ They pretend to be a customer and a clerk.

2. What clue word tells when Lara will learn about stage directions?

   Ⓐ next
   Ⓑ tomorrow
   Ⓒ last
   Ⓓ today

Work with a partner. Talk about your answers to questions 1 and 2. Tell why you chose the answers you did.

Remember: Sequence is the order in which things happen.

▮▶ Look for clue words such as *first, next, then, last, finally, before,* and *after.*

▮▶ Look for clue words that tell about times of day, days of the week, months, seasons, and years.

▮▶ In a story, think about the beginning, the middle, and the ending to understand the sequence. In an article, think about the order in which things happen or how things are done.

Read this story about a trip to see battleships. As you read, ask yourself, "What happened first? What happened next? What happened after that?" Then answer the questions.

Ships to See

James and his scout troop had waited weeks for this trip. As they exited the bus at Battleship Cove, they split into small groups.

First, James walked with his group to Newberry Hall to see the PT boats. The two PT boats there are the only ones on display in the world. James had read that President John F. Kennedy served aboard a PT boat from 1942 to 1943.

Next, James and his group boarded the *Battleship Massachusetts.* It was huge. Right away, they set out on the White Route. The White Route led visitors to the main deck and the superstructure, the part of the ship that is above the deck.

After taking this route, the group toured the second and third decks. This was called the Red Route. Then James and his group followed the Blue Route to the platform decks, the ship's boiler, and the engine rooms. When they finished, it was time to start back to the city.

3. Just before James's group took the Blue Route, they

   Ⓐ saw the engine rooms.
   Ⓑ went to see the PT boats.
   Ⓒ took the Red Route.
   Ⓓ followed the route exploring the main deck.

4. Which clue word tells what James's group explored last?

   Ⓐ after
   Ⓑ next
   Ⓒ first
   Ⓓ then

Look at the answer choices for each question.
Read why each answer choice is correct or not correct.

3. Just before James's group took the Blue Route, they

   Ⓐ saw the engine rooms.

   This answer is not correct because the story states that James and his group saw the engine rooms last, on the Blue Route.

   Ⓑ went to see the PT boats.

   This answer is not correct because the story states that the troop went to see the PT boats first, and then took the White Route.

   ● took the Red Route.

   This answer is correct because the story states that the group took the Red Route and then the Blue Route.

   Ⓓ followed the route exploring the main deck.

   This answer is not correct because it is a detail about what the group saw on the White Route. The group set out on the White Route before taking the Red Route and then the Blue Route.

4. Which clue word tells what James's group explored last?

   Ⓐ after

   This answer is not correct because the clue word after *is used to tell the next to last thing the group explored.*

   Ⓑ next

   This answer is not correct because the clue word next *appears in the third paragraph to tell what the group did second.*

   Ⓒ first

   This answer is not correct because the clue word first *tells what James and his group did first.*

   ● then

   This answer is correct because the clue word then *tells what the group explored at the end of their visit, just before it was time to start back to the city.*

PART THREE: Learn More About Sequence

Many types of reading passages present events in time order, the order in which they happened. Look for events that are presented in time order in these kinds of reading passages:

- directions and how-to paragraphs
- journal entries and diaries
- history articles

- newspaper stories
- stories, myths, fables, and folktales
- autobiographies and biographies

Read this fable by Aesop. Then answer the questions.

The Bat and the Weasels

Bat hung upside down from his tree branch. Suddenly, the wind blew hard and he fell to the ground. As Bat dusted himself off, Weasel sprang upon him. "Please spare my life!" Bat cried, not wanting to be eaten.

"I cannot," Weasel refused, "because I am by nature the enemy of all birds." Bat explained that he was not a bird but a mouse. So Weasel set him free.

Bat returned to his tree and fell asleep. After a stirring dream, Bat lost hold of the branch and fell to the ground again. Before he knew it, he was trapped by a second Weasel. "Please spare my life!" Bat cried.

"I saw my sister catch you," Weasel said. "I especially hate mice. They annoy me." He went to eat Bat.

"Oh no, I'm not really a mouse but a bat," Bat confessed. Weasel thought for a moment, then dropped Bat and ran off.

5. Which of these events happened first in the fable?

   Ⓐ The wind blew Bat from his tree.
   Ⓑ The first Weasel caught Bat.
   Ⓒ Bat had a stirring dream.
   Ⓓ Bat dusted himself off.

6. Right after Bat fell from the tree a second time,

   Ⓐ the first Weasel caught him again.
   Ⓑ the second Weasel said, "I saw my sister catch you."
   Ⓒ he was caught by a second Weasel.
   Ⓓ he explained that he was a mouse.

7. Which clue word tells what happened last?

   Ⓐ after
   Ⓑ finally
   Ⓒ then
   Ⓓ before

8. What did Bat do just before Weasel dropped him and ran off?

   Ⓐ He confessed to being a bat.
   Ⓑ He begged not to be eaten.
   Ⓒ He told Weasel that he was really a mouse.
   Ⓓ He fell from his tree.

Katherine Dunham was born in 1909 in Illinois. When she was three, her mother died. Her father sent her to Chicago. There, she lived with her aunt. Aunt Lulu took Dunham to the theater. Dunham loved the dancing. She loved the fancy costumes.

In 1914, her father brought Dunham home to Joliet, Illinois. She began school. She liked to put on musical shows with her friends. But she longed for dancing lessons. Her father thought dancing lessons were foolish, but Dunham kept asking. He finally gave in.

Dunham danced in high school and then in college in Chicago. In 1930, she opened her first dance school. She taught her students ballet. But she wanted to teach African dances. She also wanted to learn about the African roots of these dances.

In 1935, Dunham went to the West Indies. She studied dance there. Then she returned home. By 1940, she had formed her own group of black dancers. She called them the Dunham Dance Company. She moved the company to New York City. From 1947–1950, they toured many countries. They performed dances that combined African dance movements with ballet and modern dance.

In 1957, Dunham's dance company broke up. But Dunham kept her interest in dance. She wrote about her dancing. She began the Performing Arts Training Center in Illinois in 1967. Today, she still talks about her dancing.

Katherine Dunham dancing in 1956

9. In the biography, clues that tell about the sequence are
   Ⓐ days of the week.   Ⓒ years.
   Ⓑ months.   Ⓓ seasons.

10. What was Dunham doing in 1948?
   Ⓐ opening a dance school
   Ⓑ going to high school
   Ⓒ touring with her company
   Ⓓ performing in New York City

11. When did Dunham go to the West Indies?
   Ⓐ 1914   Ⓒ 1957
   Ⓑ 1935   Ⓓ 1967

12. What happened after Dunham's trip to the West Indies?
   Ⓐ She began her own school.
   Ⓑ She formed a dance company.
   Ⓒ She moved to her father's home.
   Ⓓ She went to college.

PART FOUR: Prepare for a Test

▶ A test question about sequence may ask you when certain things happened in a reading passage.

▶ A test question about sequence may ask you to put events or steps from a reading passage in order.

▶ A test question about sequence may use words such as *first, second, last, before,* or *after.*

> Here are directions for a science experiment about soil. Read the directions. Then do Numbers 13 and 14.

Have you ever noticed that when it rains in some places, the water soaks into the ground? In other places, the water forms puddles or runs mostly off the land. You can do an experiment to see why this happens.

First, get four clear jars of exactly the same shape and size. Second, collect one cupful each of sand, clay, gravel, and garden soil. Then put one kind of soil into each jar. Fill the jars to the same height. Label each jar.

Next, fill a measuring cup with two cups of water. Slowly pour the water into one of the four jars until the soil cannot hold any more water. Write down the amount of water left in the measuring cup. Then subtract this amount from the two cups you started with. This will tell you how much water the soil held.

Repeat these steps for each of the remaining jars. When you have finished, you will understand why water runs off some kinds of soil but soaks into others.

Understanding Sequence

13. What is the third step in the experiment?

Ⓐ Collect four types of soil.

Ⓑ Put one kind of soil into each jar.

Ⓒ Slowly pour water into one jar.

Ⓓ Fill a measuring cup with two cups of water.

Understanding Sequence

14. The boxes show some steps from the experiment.

Pour water into one jar.	Write down the amount of water left in the cup.	
1	2	3

Which of these belongs in box 3?

Ⓐ Repeat these steps with the remaining jars.

Ⓑ Fill the jars to the same height.

Ⓒ Subtract the amount of water left in the cup from the amount you started with.

Ⓓ Refill the measuring cup with water.

Here is an article about a mining town. Read the article.
Then do Numbers 15 and 16.

Virginia City, Nevada

During the 1800s, the search for gold and silver brought thousands of miners to the West. Several areas became busy mining centers. One such area was in Nevada.

In 1859, two miners found bits of gold in some blue Nevada soil. They were thrilled about the gold. Then they learned that the soil was pure silver! Silver was worth four thousand dollars a ton.

News of their find reached California in days. Soon, the whole country knew. Many people rushed to Nevada hoping for instant wealth.

Every day, hundreds of miners poured into the area. Some set up canvas tents. Others built rough huts. A few tucked themselves into caves in the mountains.

By 1861, the miners had founded a town. Virginia City had a population of about 15,000. Traders soon came to the area. They made a good living selling food and supplies to all the hopeful miners.

In the late 1860s, miners were digging 500 thousand dollars worth of gold and silver every month! Soon a mining company moved in and went to work.

In 1873, the company hit a vein of gold and silver. This was the richest vein ever found in the country. It held 350 million dollars worth of metals.

By the 1880s, the company closed. All the gold and silver were gone. Miners moved away. By 1900, the population of Virginia City shrank to 400.

Understanding Sequence

15. What happened within days after the two miners learned that they had discovered pure silver?

   Ⓐ The news had reached California.
   Ⓑ Hundreds of miners poured into the area daily.
   Ⓒ A mining company moved into the area.
   Ⓓ The population of Virginia City grew to 15,000.

Understanding Sequence

16. Which of these happened first?

   Ⓐ All the gold and silver were gone.
   Ⓑ Virginia City was founded.
   Ⓒ The population of Virginia City shrank to 400.
   Ⓓ The richest vein in the country was found.

1–3 Review

PART ONE: Read a Story

Here is a story based on a Japanese folktale. Read the story.
Then do Numbers 1 through 6.

One night rain poured down. Grandfather and Grandmother sat inside their house with their grandson. Grandfather looked worried.

"Do you fear anything, Grandfather?" asked the boy.

"What I fear is a thief," Grandfather answered.

Grandfather did not know a thief had crawled onto his roof. The thief, who planned to steal a cow, felt proud to be so feared.

After a few minutes, the boy asked another question. "What animal are you most afraid of Grandfather?" the boy asked.

"The wolf," Grandfather answered.

Grandfather did not know a wolf was prowling his yard for chickens. The wolf puffed up with pride at the fear he stirred up.

"More than a thief or a wolf, what are you most afraid of?" the boy asked.

Grandfather looked up at his roof. "Now, I most fear a leak! It might come at any moment."

Both the thief and the wolf wondered about this horrible creature that could cause more fear than they could. They worried that a leak would come right then.

The anxious thief lost his footing. He slipped off the roof and dropped with a howl of pain onto the wolf. The wolf yelped, thinking a leak had hit him. The thief grasped the wolf's wet fur, and the wolf ran off with the thief still holding on.

Panting, the wolf raced hard through the woods, hoping the leak would fall off his back. The thief held tight until he could safely grab onto a tree branch. The wolf ran on to get far from the leak. The thief stayed in the tree until morning. Both the wolf and the thief now feared the leak most of all.

Finding Main Idea

1. The best title for the story is

Ⓐ "The Terrifying Leak."

Ⓑ "A Grandmother's Foolish Questions."

Ⓒ "The Thief and the Wolf."

Ⓓ "Grandfather and the Leak in the Roof."

Finding Main Idea

2. The main idea of the story is found

Ⓐ in the first sentence of the first paragraph.

Ⓑ in the last sentence of the first paragraph.

Ⓒ in the last paragraph.

Ⓓ by thinking about the most important idea in the story.

Recalling Facts and Details

3. What was the wolf looking for at Grandfather's house?

Ⓐ cows

Ⓑ chickens

Ⓒ grandchildren

Ⓓ leaks

Recalling Facts and Details

4. Which detail shows that the thief was nervous?

Ⓐ He crawled onto the roof.

Ⓑ He slipped off the roof.

Ⓒ He was proud to be so feared.

Ⓓ He planned to steal a cow.

Understanding Sequence

5. The boxes tell about some things that happened in the story.

Grandfather said that he feared a leak.	The thief and wolf wondered what kind of horrible creature a leak was.	
1	2	3

Which of these belongs in box 3?

Ⓐ Grandfather looked worried.

Ⓑ The thief grabbed onto a tree branch.

Ⓒ The wolf puffed up with pride.

Ⓓ The boy asked his grandfather what animal he feared most.

Understanding Sequence

6. What happens right after Grandfather answers the first question?

Ⓐ The boy asks a second question.

Ⓑ Grandfather mentions the leak.

Ⓒ The wolf appears in the yard.

Ⓓ The thief feels proud.

Here is an article about empires in West Africa. Read the article.
Then do Numbers 7 through 12.

Long ago, West Africa had a fortunate location for trading. The Sahara, to the north, was rich in salt. Here traders dug salt from the desert and traveled south to trade. The traders met merchants in West Africa and exchanged the salt for gold. South of West Africa were gold mines. The owners kept the locations of the mines secret. But the rulers controlled the meeting place of the salt traders and the gold traders. They grew wealthy by charging a tax on items traded. Rulers used this money to build their kingdoms. Over time, West Africa had three great empires. They were Ghana, Mali, and Songhai.

In the 300s, Ghana controlled the trading of gold and salt. The king of Ghana collected taxes. Merchants who traveled through Ghana with salt paid a tax. Traders who went back to the north paid a tax on the gold they had received for their salt. The king also claimed all gold nuggets found in his kingdom. Ghana became a great kingdom.

By the mid-1000s, the Ghana Empire came under attack. People from the north invaded the capital. Ghana fell.

Soon the Mali Empire rose from the dust of Ghana. During the 1200s, Mali controlled the rich trade of salt and gold. A great ruler called Mansa Musa took power in 1312. He collected a tax on every bag of salt or gold that crossed into Mali. His kingdom grew larger than Ghana had been.

Mali came under attack in the late 1400s by the Songhai. By 1500, the Songhai Empire controlled most of the Mali Empire. Songhai's first ruler gained much land. Future rulers added more. For about a hundred years, Songhai grew rich from the gold and salt trade. Finally, people from North Africa conquered the Songhai. The Songhai Empire ended in 1591.

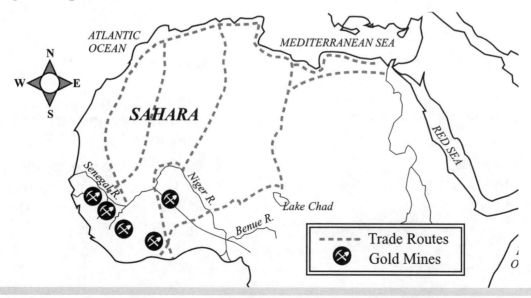

Finding Main Idea

7. Which of these is a good title for the article?

   Ⓐ "The Rule of Mansa Musa"
   Ⓑ "Empires from Gold and Salt"
   Ⓒ "The Secret Mines"
   Ⓓ "The End of the Salt Trade"

Recalling Facts and Details

10. What did the king of Ghana claim for himself?

   Ⓐ all the salt passing through Ghana
   Ⓑ any gold nuggets found in his kingdom
   Ⓒ all the gold collected by merchants
   Ⓓ several bags of salt and gold from each trader

Finding Main Idea

8. What is the main idea of the first paragraph?

   Ⓐ Traders dug salt from the Sahara.
   Ⓑ Long ago, West Africa had a fortunate location for trading.
   Ⓒ Rulers controlled the meeting place of the salt traders and the gold traders.
   Ⓓ West Africa had three great empires.

Understanding Sequence

11. Which was the first great kingdom of West Africa?

   Ⓐ Sahara
   Ⓑ Mali
   Ⓒ Songhai
   Ⓓ Ghana

Recalling Facts and Details

9. Mansa Musa was a ruler of

   Ⓐ all of West Africa.
   Ⓑ Songhai.
   Ⓒ Ghana.
   Ⓓ Mali.

Understanding Sequence

12. You can tell the sequence in the article mostly by

   Ⓐ looking for clue words such as *next, then,* or *finally*.
   Ⓑ thinking about the main idea.
   Ⓒ looking for clue words such as dates and time periods.
   Ⓓ noticing the article goes from the last event in time to the first.

4 Recognizing Cause and Effect

PART ONE: Learn About Cause and Effect

> Read this letter of complaint that Rene wrote. What happened to Rene is underlined. Read to find why it happened.

Harvest Booksellers
10 Apple Street
Maryville, TN 37801

Dear Harvest Booksellers:

    I recently ordered a book from your company. The book I received, however, was not the one I ordered. I have checked my letter, and I had correctly stated that I wanted the book *The Cats of Time*. The book I received was *The Cast of Time*.

    Someone read my letter wrong and typed in the wrong title on the order form. As a result, <u>I received the wrong book.</u> Please let me know what to do with the book I received, and send me the one I wanted.

Sincerely,
Rene A. Manx

What happened to Rene and why?

What happened: **Rene received the wrong book.**
Why it happened: **Someone read the letter wrong and typed in the wrong title on the order form.**

What happens and why is called **cause and effect**.
Why something happens is the **cause**. *Someone read the letter wrong and typed in the wrong title on the order form.*
What happens because of the cause is the **effect**. *Rene received the wrong book.*

▮▶ A cause is the reason that something happens.

▮▶ An effect is what happens because of the cause.

▮▶ Clue words such as *so, so that, since, because,* and *if* often signal cause and effect. Other clue words are *reason* and *as a result*.

Read this article about skyscrapers. As you read, look for clue words to help you understand what happened and why it happened. Then answer the questions.

Going Up!

During the late 1800s, people flocked to growing American cities. Here, they hoped to find jobs and housing. Cities were already crowded. Large buildings covered nearly all the land. New buildings were needed. But there was not much available land to build on.

Some architects had a new idea. Since there was so little land to build structures that spread out, what about building upward? They designed tall buildings. These new styles needed little ground space because they had many floors. The first skyscrapers were born! As a result, more living and working space opened up for the city's people.

By the 1930s, New York City had many skyscrapers.

1. Architects decided to build upward because
   Ⓐ they had plenty of ground to build on.
   Ⓑ the land to build on was almost gone.
   Ⓒ they did not need to add many floors.
   Ⓓ they wanted to make the city less crowded.

2. Which clue word or words signal what happened when architects built the first skyscrapers?
   Ⓐ because
   Ⓑ since
   Ⓒ reason
   Ⓓ as a result

Work with a partner. Talk about your answers to questions 1 and 2. Tell why you chose the answers you did.

Remember: A cause is the reason something happens. An effect is the result, or what happens.

▶ To find a cause, look for the reason something happened.
Ask yourself, "*Why* did this happen?"

▶ To find an effect, look for the result, or the thing that happened.
Ask yourself, "*What* happened?"

▶ Look for clue words that can signal cause and effect, such as *so, so that, since, because, if, reason,* and *as a result.*

> Read this sports article about a tennis match. As you read, ask yourself, "*What* events happened? *Why* did they happen?" Then answer the questions.

When Li Chan faced Carlotta Sanchez last Friday, the stakes were high. The championship would go to the winner.

The final minutes of play excited the crowd. Li paced tensely behind the net since the score was tied. Both players had already won two games. The winner of this game would win both the match and the championship.

Carlotta swung her racket upward and served the ball, which flew briskly over the net. Li decided to return the ball by hitting toward Carlotta's left side because, so far, Carlotta had missed only shots to her left. The decision paid off. Carlotta missed the ball. Li scored one point. On the next serve, Li hit again to Carlotta's left. Carlotta missed, so Li won the championship. The players shook hands and walked off the court.

3. Why did Li hit to Carlotta's left?

Ⓐ Li did not know how to hit to Carlotta's right.

Ⓑ Carlotta had missed only shots to her left.

Ⓒ Carlotta swung her racket upward to serve the ball.

Ⓓ Li hoped to make the final minutes of play exciting.

4. Li paced tensely behind the net because

Ⓐ Carlotta's serve flew briskly over the net.

Ⓑ she was facing the best tennis player in the match.

Ⓒ she had lost the previous game.

Ⓓ the score was tied.

Look at the answer choices for each question.
Read why each answer choice is correct or not correct.

3. Why did Li hit to Carlotta's left?

   Ⓐ Li did not know how to hit to Carlotta's right.

   This answer is not correct because nothing is said about Li's ability to hit to Carlotta's right. Also, the article mentions that Carlotta missed only the shots to her left, suggesting that Li must have hit some shots to Carlotta's right.

   ● Carlotta had missed only shots to her left.

   This answer is correct because the article states "Li decided to return the ball by hitting toward Carlotta's left side because, so far, Carlotta had missed only shots to her left."

   Ⓒ Carlotta swung her racket upward to serve the ball.

   This answer is not correct because the way Carlotta served the ball had nothing to do with Li's decision to hit toward Carlotta's left.

   Ⓓ Li hoped to make the final minutes of play exciting.

   This answer is not correct because there is nothing in the article that states Li wanted to make the final minutes of play exciting. Also, the article states "The final minutes of play excited the crowd." The play is already exciting to the crowd.

4. Li paced tensely behind the net because

   Ⓐ Carlotta's serve flew briskly over the net.

   This answer is not correct because Li paced before Carlotta served. Carlotta's serve is not the reason for Li's tenseness.

   Ⓑ she was facing the best tennis player in the match.

   This answer is not correct because the article never states who was the best tennis player in the match. The reader cannot tell who was considered the best tennis player in the match. It could have been Carlotta or Li. After the match, the winner, Li, could be called the best player.

   Ⓒ she had lost the previous game.

   This answer is not correct because the article does not say who lost the previous game. It could have been either player, since each player had won two games.

   ● the score was tied.

   This answer is correct because the article states "Li paced tensely behind the net since the score was tied." Li knew that the winner of the game would also win the match and the championship.

PART THREE: Learn More About Cause and Effect

Sometimes, writers do not use clue words to signal cause and effect. When there are no clue words to help you, you can still ask yourself the same questions.

▪▶ To find an effect, ask yourself, "*What* happened?"

▪▶ To find a cause, ask yourself, "*Why* did this happen?" or "*What* made it happen?"

▪▶ Think about what you already know about how one thing causes another thing to happen.

> **Read this speech a student wrote about Thanksgiving. Then answer the questions.**

Native people held harvest festivals long before the Pilgrims came to this country. Yet, we credit the Pilgrims with the first Thanksgiving. In the fall of 1621, because of a good harvest, the Pilgrims held a feast. They gave thanks for their blessings. They shared this feast with about 90 Native Americans.

Thanksgiving was made a yearly holiday in 1863. The holiday was celebrated on the last Thursday in November. In 1939, President Franklin D. Roosevelt changed the date. He made the holiday one week earlier. Shop owners wanted an extra week between Thanksgiving and Christmas so that people would have more time to shop. But many people were unhappy with the change. Then Congress stepped in. They made Thanksgiving the fourth Thursday in November. Thanksgiving now falls on the last Thursday in November five out of seven years. That means that some years still have a longer holiday shopping season than others.

5. Why did President Roosevelt make Thanksgiving one week earlier?

Ⓐ Shop owners wanted more time for people to shop for Christmas.
Ⓑ People wanted the date changed.
Ⓒ He wanted the date to match that of the first Thanksgiving.
Ⓓ Shoppers wanted the date changed.

6. The reason Congress stepped in was

Ⓐ no one celebrated the holiday.
Ⓑ people didn't do extra shopping.
Ⓒ shop owners disliked the change.
Ⓓ many people were against the change.

7. Why did the Pilgrims hold a feast in 1621?

Ⓐ to celebrate their arrival from Europe
Ⓑ to make friends with the Native Americans
Ⓒ because they had a good harvest
Ⓓ because they had seen native people holding harvest celebrations

8. Which clue word or words signal the reason shop owners wanted the date of Thanksgiving changed?

Ⓐ because
Ⓑ as a result
Ⓒ so that
Ⓓ reason

Read this essay about how people keep cool. Then answer the questions.

When Air Heats Up

Living in a region of high heat requires ways of cooling off. The human body already has its own cooling system. When it is hot, people sweat. Sweating produces water. The water dries on the skin so that a person feels cooler.

People have also learned to use technology for cooling. In the American Southwest, some people build houses with thick adobe walls. The walls keep the heat out and the house remains cool inside. The windows are small and high. Hot air rises and flows out during the day. Cool air is heavier so it sinks and flows in at night.

In the world's coastal areas, people carefully place buildings where they catch the cooling sea breeze. In the Middle East, tall wind towers help bring the wind down into the living area. In India, people hang wet reed mats in doorways. As the water evaporates from the mat, the air cools.

Many modern buildings use electrical air conditioning units. The effect is drier, cooler air at the touch of a switch.

9. What happens when people use air conditioning units?
   Ⓐ Breezes blow through their homes.
   Ⓑ The inside air becomes cooler and drier.
   Ⓒ Water evaporates and cools the air.
   Ⓓ Hot air rises and flows outside.

10. Why do people near the coast carefully select the location for buildings?
    Ⓐ The land doesn't support thick walls.
    Ⓑ They want to see the ocean.
    Ⓒ They want to catch the cooling sea breeze.
    Ⓓ They want to be sure the buildings aren't too close to the water.

11. Which clue word or words signal a cause and effect in paragraph one?
    Ⓐ so that
    Ⓑ so
    Ⓒ if
    Ⓓ since

12. In the evening, why does cool air sink through the small, high windows of an adobe home?
    Ⓐ Cool air is light and fresh.
    Ⓑ Cool air is heavier than hot air.
    Ⓒ Cool air always comes with a breeze.
    Ⓓ Cool air can move along the thick adobe walls.

▯▶ A test question about cause and effect may ask you *what* happened in a reading passage (the effect).

▯▶ A test question about cause and effect may ask you *why* something happened in a reading passage (the cause).

▯▶ A test question about cause and effect may contain the words *why, what happened, reason, result,* or *because.*

Here is a poem about nature. Read the poem. Then do Numbers 13 and 14.

At Dawn

The birds sing for the sun to rise.
I listen because I want to hear,
Above the chatter of chickadees,
The crush of the brush by a deer.

My open window greets the air,
So I can hear the slightest sound.
Outside, a branch snaps in the brush,
So I rush to the window to look around.

I saw the deer a week ago,
Hurrying by with its little fawn.
I'd like again to see it pass;
It only comes at dusk or dawn.

I strain my eyes, I look in vain.
A gentle rain begins to fall.
The sun drops back behind the clouds;
I see the raindrops, that is all.

Recognizing Cause and Effect

13. Why does the narrator listen carefully in the morning?
    Ⓐ She wants to hear chickadees.
    Ⓑ She is hoping to hear the sounds of a deer.
    Ⓒ She likes to hear the rain on her window.
    Ⓓ She is waiting for her alarm to go off.

Recognizing Cause and Effect

14. The narrator looks outside because
    Ⓐ it has begun to rain.
    Ⓑ she hears the wind blowing.
    Ⓒ she hears a snapping sound.
    Ⓓ the chickadees are singing.

Here is a story from Fiji, an island in the South Pacific. Read the story. Then do Numbers 15 and 16.

A Quick and Clever Solution

Everyone in the village liked Tautavaya-O because he was a quick thinker, a good talker, and open to all. Even the animals liked him.

The king had been having trouble. Chickens in his land wandered noisily. Since the boy was so clever, the king asked him to care for the chickens.

Pleased, the boy spoke to the chickens, telling them he would keep them safe and comfortable. He would help them find food. Because of his words and his actions, the chickens obeyed the boy.

One day, the boy saw a reef appear when the tide went out. He swam to the reef and then called the chickens to join him. When they arrived, they found juicy worms to eat.

The boy returned to the water and, unfortunately, stepped into a giant clam. The clam clamped down and the boy could not move. The tide washed the edges of the reef. The boy pleaded with the clam, but the clam would not let him go. Bravely, the boy told the chickens to fly home. They refused, and they circled around making a horrible racket. The boy paused and thought. Then he said to the clam, "I know you are an oyster."

"Why do you say that?" the clam asked unbelievingly.

"Because I can feel a pearl with my foot," the boy said. "Only oysters have pearls."

The clam was confused, but the boy was so convincing that the clam opened its shell to prove there was no pearl. The boy pulled his foot out and swam to shore with his chickens happily flapping over his head.

Recognizing Cause and Effect

15. The king asked the boy to care for the chickens because

   Ⓐ the boy was clever.

   Ⓑ the king was jealous that so many people liked the boy.

   Ⓒ the king could no longer care for the chickens himself.

   Ⓓ the boy could talk to the chickens and get them to obey.

Recognizing Cause and Effect

16. What was the result of the boy's claiming to feel a pearl?

   Ⓐ The clam became convinced that it was an oyster.

   Ⓑ The chickens circled around the boy.

   Ⓒ The clam opened its shell to prove there was no pearl.

   Ⓓ The boy finally earned the trust of the chickens.

Comparing and Contrasting

PART ONE: Learn About Comparing and Contrasting

Read this article about doing laundry. The underlined sentences tell how washing clothes in the past is like washing clothes today. Read to find the ways that washing clothes in the past is different from washing clothes today.

In the early 1900s, <u>many people washed their clothes at home</u>. People spent hours doing laundry by hand. <u>The clothes were cleaned in a tub of soapy water.</u> The clothes were scrubbed clean on a rough washboard. <u>The clothes were then rinsed in a tub of clean water.</u>

Today, <u>many people wash their clothes at home</u>. But today, people use a washing machine that runs on electricity. <u>The clothes are cleaned in a tub of soapy water.</u> The clothes are scrubbed clean by an agitator in the machine. The dirty water is drained and the machine fills with clean water. <u>The clothes are then rinsed in a tub of clean water.</u>

Here are ways in which washing clothes in the past is like washing clothes today:
Many people washed their clothes at home.
The clothes were cleaned in a tub of soapy water.
The clothes were then rinsed in a tub of clean water.

Here are ways in which washing clothes in the past is different from washing clothes today:
People spent hours doing laundry by hand.
The clothes were scrubbed clean on a rough washboard.

Finding how two or more things are alike and how they are different is called **comparing and contrasting**. Comparing is finding how things are alike. Contrasting is finding how things are different.

▶ Clue words that signal how things are alike include *both, same, like, alike,* and *similar.*

▶ Clue words that signal how things are different are *but, unlike, different,* and *however.*

▶ People, places, objects, and events can all be compared and contrasted.

Read this article about a pair of twins. As you read, look for clue words that tell how the boys are alike and how they are different. Then answer the questions.

Not Two Peas in a Pod

Tim and Tom are twins. They both have the same parents and were born on the same day, just a few moments apart. At birth, Tim and Tom weighed about the same, but Tom was almost an inch longer.

As the boys grew, they became more different than alike. Now, at age fifteen, Tim is 5 feet 4 inches tall, while Tom stretches to 5 feet 10 inches. Tim, who asked his friends to call him Timothy, likes neatly ironed shirts and black pants. Like Tim, Tom asked to be called by a different name. However, he chose Tommy, not Thomas. He dresses in T-shirts and jeans all year long.

1. How are Tim and Tom alike at fifteen-years-old?

Ⓐ Both are the same height.
Ⓑ Both asked to be called a different name.
Ⓒ Both wear neatly ironed shirts.
Ⓓ Both dress in jeans all year long.

2. Which clue word signals a difference about the boys when they were babies?

Ⓐ different
Ⓑ however
Ⓒ both
Ⓓ but

Work with a partner. Talk about your answers to questions 1 and 2. Tell why you chose the answers you did.

PART TWO: Check Your Understanding

**Remember: Comparing is finding ways in which things are alike.
Contrasting is finding ways in which things are different.**

▮▶ Look for clue words that signal a likeness, or comparison, such as *both,
same, like, alike,* and *similar.*

▮▶ Look for clue words that signal a difference, or contrast, such as *but, unlike,
different,* and *however.*

▮▶ Look for people, places, objects, and events that are being compared and contrasted.

Read this article about two types of underwater diving. As you read, ask
yourself, "How are these types of diving alike? How are they different?"
Then answer the questions.

For deep-sea diving, divers wear suits with helmets. To provide air to breathe,
air hoses run from a ship at the surface to the diver's suit. But if you want to
swim underwater without such equipment, you have two choices. Neither choice
will give you protection from the high pressure of the deep ocean. So you can't
go deep!

The first choice is free diving. This kind of diving is called free diving because
divers are free to swim wherever they want. Hoses do not tie them to the
surface. However, most free divers can only go down 30 to 40 feet. They can
stay underwater only for as long as they can hold their breath. There isn't time
to see much!

Unlike free divers, scuba divers do not hold their breath. They breathe from
tanks that are filled with special air. Like free diving, there are no hoses attached
to a ship at the surface. Most scuba divers dive about 100 feet. Once they reach
that depth, they do not have to surface right away. They can explore the ocean
floor for about half an hour.

3. What is one way that free diving
and scuba diving are alike?

   Ⓐ Both require air tanks.
   Ⓑ Both are safe in the deep ocean.
   Ⓒ Both allow divers to explore the
   ocean floor for about half an hour.
   Ⓓ Both do not use air hoses that run
   from a ship.

4. Which clue word signals how
scuba divers breathe differently
than free divers?

   Ⓐ like
   Ⓑ unlike
   Ⓒ but
   Ⓓ different

Look at the answer choices for each question.
Read why each answer choice is correct or not correct.

3. What is one way that free diving and scuba diving are alike?

   Ⓐ Both require air tanks.
   This answer is not correct because free divers do not use tanks. They simply hold their breath to go underwater.

   Ⓑ Both are safe in the deep ocean.
   This answer is not correct because neither type of diving is safe in the deep ocean. Neither type of diving provides protection from the high pressure of the deep ocean.

   Ⓒ Both allow divers to explore the ocean floor for about half an hour.
   This answer is not correct because only scuba diving allows divers to explore the ocean floor for about half an hour. Free divers can stay underwater only for as long as they can hold their breath.

   ● Both do not use air hoses that run from a ship.
   This answer is correct because the article states that free divers hold their breath and that "Hoses do not tie them to the surface." About scuba divers, the article states, "Like free diving, there are no hoses attached to a ship at the surface." The clue word like *signals a likeness.*

4. Which clue word signals how scuba divers breathe differently than free divers?

   Ⓐ like
   This answer is not correct because the clue word like *is usually used to compare things, not contrast them. In the article, the word* like *points out that the two types of diving are alike in that there are no hoses attached to a ship at the surface.*

   ● unlike
   This answer is correct because the clue word unlike *contrasts the different ways scuba divers and free divers hold their breath. The article states "Unlike free divers, scuba divers do not hold their breath."*

   Ⓒ but
   This answer is not correct because, although the clue word but *can suggest a contrast, it is used in the first paragraph to contrast how other kinds of diving are different than deep-sea diving.*

   Ⓓ different
   This answer is not correct because the clue word different *is not used in the article.*

PART THREE: Learn More About Comparing and Contrasting

Sometimes, there are no clue words in a reading passage to signal that things are being compared or contrasted. When there are no clue words,

▪▶ think about the people, places, objects, or events that you are reading about. Ask yourself, "How are they alike? How are they different?"

▪▶ think about the people, places, objects, or events that you are reading about. Ask yourself, "What things are compared or contrasted? In what ways are they compared? In what ways are they contrasted?"

Read this science article about turtles. Then answer the questions.

A turtle is a kind of reptile that has a hard protective shell on its back. Turtles are cold-blooded animals that hatch from eggs. All turtles lay their eggs on land.

Both sea turtles and tortoises are turtles. The seven kinds of sea turtles live in warm ocean water. Their shells are designed for fast swimming. Their legs are like paddles, with flippers for feet. Sea turtles cannot pull in their head and legs for safety the way other turtles can. Sea turtles migrate great distances. Most sea turtles eat both plant and animal material.

The 50 kinds of tortoises live on land. They have heavy, short legs and crawl slowly, but they do not go far. Their shells are high domes with lots of room to hide. Unlike most sea turtles, tortoises eat only plants.

5. What is one way that sea turtles and tortoises are alike?

Ⓐ They both are turtles.
Ⓑ They both have flippers for feet.
Ⓒ They both live in the water.
Ⓓ They both have heavy, short legs.

6. What is one way that sea turtles and tortoises are different?

Ⓐ Sea turtles have a hard shell, but tortoises have a soft shell.
Ⓑ Sea turtles do not migrate, but tortoises do.
Ⓒ Sea turtles cannot hide in their shells, but tortoises can.
Ⓓ Sea turtles are cold-blooded, but tortoises are warm-blooded.

7. What is one way that tortoises are like sea turtles?

Ⓐ Tortoises live on land.
Ⓑ Tortoises move quickly.
Ⓒ Tortoises have domed shells.
Ⓓ Tortoises lay their eggs on land.

8. Which clue word signals a difference in the foods that tortoises and sea turtles eat?

Ⓐ both
Ⓑ but
Ⓒ unlike
Ⓓ however

Read this chart about the planets Saturn and Jupiter. Then answer the questions.

Facts	Saturn	Jupiter
Orbits our sun	✓	✓
Named for a Roman god	✓	✓
Is among the largest planets	✓	✓
Made mostly of hydrogen and helium	✓	✓
Has a small solid or liquid center	✓	✓
Has 300 times more mass than Earth		✓
Is among the outer planets	✓	✓
Is known as a Jovian planet	✓	✓
Has more than 20 known moons	✓	
Has the largest moon in the solar system		✓
Has a moon with active volcanoes		✓
Has a system of rings	✓	✓
Revolves around the sun every $29\frac{1}{2}$ years	✓	
Rotates faster than any other planet		✓
Is known for its Great Red Spot		✓
Is known for its seven large rings	✓	

9. Which of these tells one way that Saturn is different from Jupiter?

Ⓐ Saturn was named for a Roman god.

Ⓑ Saturn is a Jovian planet.

Ⓒ Saturn has 300 times more mass than Earth.

Ⓓ Saturn revolves around the sun every $29\frac{1}{2}$ years.

10. One way that Saturn and Jupiter are alike is that they each

Ⓐ have a small solid or liquid center.

Ⓑ have seven large rings.

Ⓒ have moons with active volcanoes.

Ⓓ have a Great Red Spot.

11. Which fact makes Jupiter different from Saturn?

Ⓐ Jupiter rotates faster than any other planet.

Ⓑ Jupiter orbits our sun.

Ⓒ Jupiter is made mostly of hydrogen and helium.

Ⓓ Jupiter is among the outer planets.

12. Which statement is true?

Ⓐ Jupiter and Saturn are different in more ways than they are alike.

Ⓑ Jupiter has all the qualities Saturn has and more.

Ⓒ Saturn is just like Jupiter except it has more rings and more moons.

Ⓓ Jupiter and Saturn are alike in as many ways as they are different.

- A test question about comparing and contrasting may ask you how things are alike or how they are different.

- A test question about comparing and contrasting usually contains a clue word. Words such as *same*, *like*, *alike*, and *similar* signal that you are to compare things. Words such as *different*, *unlike*, or *not like* signal that you are to contrast things.

Here is a letter about a visit to an art museum. Read the letter. Then do Numbers 13 and 14.

Dear Aunt Jessie,

I know you love paintings. We just came back from a museum where I studied painters. My two favorites were John Constable and Winslow Homer.

Constable was an English painter. He lived from 1776 to 1837. He had been painting for many years before his work gained attention. That was because he was a nature painter, when most artists of his time painted people. Many of his scenes are of quiet fields and woodlands. His details are fine. The custom of his time was to paint muddy, dark landscapes. But his landscapes were full of green and other bright colors.

Homer, an American, was born a year before Constable died. He gained attention early in his career. His works of American country life and of war sold well. He moved to England and began painting the sea. Two years later, he moved back to America and settled in Maine. At first, his new sea paintings showed people facing heavy waves and fighting for life in sinking ships. His later paintings show only the empty sea, often raging in storms.

I'd like to hear what you have to say about these painters. Please write soon.

Love,
Caroline

Comparing and Contrasting

13. In what way were Homer's later paintings similar to Constable's?

Ⓐ The paintings were pictures of fields.
Ⓑ The paintings were not of people.
Ⓒ The paintings had bright colors.
Ⓓ The paintings showed American country life.

Comparing and Contrasting

14. Homer was different from Constable because Homer

Ⓐ gained attention near the start of his career.
Ⓑ lived in England.
Ⓒ painted scenes of natural beauty.
Ⓓ was alive in 1836.

Here is a Native-American folktale from the Northwest coast. Read the folktale. Then do Numbers 15 and 16.

Good Friends

Beaver and Porcupine were friends. They often visited each other's homes. But Beaver was growing annoyed with Porcupine's visits. When Porcupine left, Beaver had to clean up all the nasty quills Porcupine had dropped.

One day Porcupine suggested, "Let's go to your home."

Beaver answered, "I'll take you on my back." Porcupine jumped on Beaver. Instead of carrying him to his home, Beaver swam into the lake. He dropped Porcupine on a stump in the very middle. "Do you like my new home?" Beaver called out as he swam away.

Porcupine was stranded. So he started to sing, "Let the waters freeze." Because Porcupine had magic, the waters froze and he walked to shore.

The next time the friends were playing, Porcupine urged, "Jump on my back and I'll carry you." Beaver jumped on.

Porcupine hurried up a tall tree. He carried Beaver to the very top. He dropped him on a branch and scurried down. For a long time, Beaver was stuck in that tree, but he finally managed to climb down. When he did, he scratched up the bark so badly that every tree grew scratchy bark from then on.

Comparing and Contrasting

15. How were Beaver and Porcupine alike in the folktale?

   Ⓐ Both swam well.
   Ⓑ Both were good at climbing trees.
   Ⓒ Both played a trick.
   Ⓓ Both made a mess in the other's home.

Comparing and Contrasting

16. What is one way Beaver was different from Porcupine?

   Ⓐ Beaver used his own skills to save himself, but Porcupine used magic.
   Ⓑ Beaver hesitated getting onto Porcupine's back, but Porcupine jumped right onto Beaver's back.
   Ⓒ Beaver never visited Porcupine's home, but Porcupine often visited Beaver's home.
   Ⓓ Beaver tricked Porcupine because he was annoyed, but Porcupine had no reason to trick Beaver.

Making Predictions

PART ONE: Learn About Making Predictions

Read this story about a math class. As you read, think about what might happen next in the story.

Where's Mr. McGowan?

Twenty-nine students filed into room 101 for math class. Most days, the teacher sat at his desk that was covered with everything from papers to student projects. Today, the desk was clean. Mr. McGowan was not sitting there. Most of the students dropped into their seats. They looked toward the door, expecting someone to enter. Finally, the door opened. A stern looking stranger stepped into the room.

Think about what you read and what you already know about school classes. Make a good guess about what might happen next. Then continue reading to see how close your guess is to what actually happens.

The stranger spoke to the class. "Mr. McGowan is out sick today. I am your substitute teacher, Miss Strict. My name says it all!" she added firmly. "Let's get to work."

What happened next in the story was **the stranger spoke to the class.**

When you think about what might happen next in a reading passage, you are **making a prediction**. Making a prediction is a way of using clues from a reading passage, as well as things you already know, to make a good guess about what might happen next.

- ▣ Clues are often in the title of a reading passage. Read the title, and then make a prediction about what you will be reading.

- ▣ Clues are often in the facts and details in a reading passage. Details about the things characters do and say often help you make a prediction about what they might do or say later in the story.

- ▣ Clues are often in any pictures included with a story. Pictures often show something that is happening or will happen soon.

Read this Greek myth. As you read, ask yourself, "What does the title tell me about what I will be reading? Which facts and details will help me predict what will happen next?" Then answer the questions.

Killing the Minotaur

King Minos lived on the island of Crete. Every year, the people of Athens, a Greek city, had to send seven young men and seven young women to King Minos. The king ordered these people into his maze. The maze had many connected pathways. Once people went inside the maze, they got lost and couldn't find the pathway out. In the maze, the king kept a beast called the Minotaur. It was half bull and half human. The people were food for the Minotaur.

The citizens of Athens hated giving up their young people to King Minos's horrible beast. So one year, Theseus, son of the king of Athens, decided to go to Crete with the young people. The daughter of Minos liked Theseus, so she gave him a knife to kill the beast. She also gave him thread. Inside the maze, Theseus could unwind the thread. To find his way out of the maze, he could follow the thread. Theseus was brave, strong, and clever. When he set off into the maze, he knew he could save his people.

1. What will most likely happen next?

Ⓐ Minos's daughter will follow Theseus into the maze.

Ⓑ King Minos will order the young people to leave the maze.

Ⓒ Theseus will kill the Minotaur and lead his people out of the maze.

Ⓓ The Minotaur will eat Theseus and follow the thread out of the maze.

2. Where did you find clues to help you make your prediction?

Ⓐ in the description of King Minos and his maze

Ⓑ in the title and the details about Theseus and King Minos's daughter

Ⓒ in the picture included with the story

Ⓓ in the details about the seven young men and seven young women

Work with a partner. Talk about your answers to questions 1 and 2. Tell why you chose the answers you did.

Remember: **Making a prediction is a way of using clues from a reading passage, as well as things you already know, to make a good guess about what might happen next.**

▶ Look for clues in a reading passage to help you predict what might happen next. Clues are often in the title, in the facts and details, and in any pictures.

▶ Ask yourself, "What do I already know about the things I am reading about?"

Read this fable from Aesop. As you read, look for clues that will help you predict the ending of the fable. Then answer the questions.

The Lion and the Mouse

Proud, brave Lion was asleep, so his strong, heavy limbs were relaxed. He was dreaming about a fine meal.

Mouse, honest and curious, crawled up over Lion's shoulder. Mouse's tiny feet carried him onto Lion's face. Lion's whiskers twitched and his eyes blinked open.

"Mouse, I shall eat you for walking on me," Lion roared.

"Please don't eat me," Mouse begged. "I will pay you back if you let me go." Mouse did not make promises lightly.

"A mouse pay back a lion!" Lion laughed, thinking how small a mouse is compared to his own greatness. Yet, moved by Mouse's boldness, he let Mouse go.

The next morning, Lion was walking in the forest when he was caught in a hunter's net. Mouse heard Lion howl and scurried toward the sound.

3. What will probably happen as soon as Mouse reaches Lion?

　Ⓐ Mouse will laugh at Lion and run off to play.

　Ⓑ Mouse will help Lion escape by chewing the net.

　Ⓒ Lion will now eat Mouse.

　Ⓓ Lion will cry and beg to be set free.

4. If Lion had not let Mouse go,

　Ⓐ Lion might not have been caught in the hunter's net.

　Ⓑ the ending of the fable would still be the same.

　Ⓒ Mouse would not have gone to see what happened to Lion.

　Ⓓ Mouse would have bit Lion with his sharp teeth.

Look at the answer choices for each question.
Read why each answer choice is correct or not correct.

3. What will probably happen as soon as Mouse reaches Lion?

   Ⓐ Mouse will laugh at Lion and run off to play.

   This answer is not correct because clues from the fable suggest that Mouse plans to repay lion for not eating him. The fable tells you that Mouse is honest and does not make promises lightly.

   ● Mouse will help Lion escape by chewing the net.

   This answer is correct because Mouse plans to repay Lion. Saving Lion's life would repay him for having let Mouse go. You probably also know that mice have teeth that are good for chewing things.

   Ⓒ Lion will now eat Mouse.

   This answer is not correct because Lion is caught in a net and cannot get free. He could not eat Mouse now even if he wanted to.

   Ⓓ Lion will cry and beg to be set free.

   This answer is not correct because details in the fable describe Lion as being proud and brave. He is not likely to cry or to beg for his life.

4. If Lion had not let Mouse go,

   Ⓐ Lion might not have been caught in the hunter's net.

   This answer is not correct because there are no clues in the fable to suggest that Lion's being caught by the net has anything to do with what happened earlier with Mouse.

   Ⓑ the ending of the fable would still be the same.

   This answer is not correct because the whole fable would have changed. If Lion had eaten Mouse, Mouse would not have been around to hear Lion's howl. Lion would have been on his own.

   ● Mouse would not have gone to see what happened to Lion.

   This answer is correct because if Lion had not let Mouse go, Mouse would have been eaten by Lion before Lion became caught in the net.

   Ⓓ Mouse would have bit Lion with his sharp teeth.

   This answer is not correct because Mouse would have been eaten. Also, Mouse had promised to repay Lion. Biting Lion would not be a way for Mouse to repay him.

PART THREE: Learn More About Making Predictions

▶ Look for clues in the reading passage that tell what the characters are like. Think about how the characters behave, how they are feeling, and the things they say and do.

▶ Link the clues with what you know from your own experiences. Ask yourself, "What have people like this character done in a similar situation?"

Read this book report. Then answer the questions.

Mrs. Frisby and the Rats of NIMH by Robert C. O'Brien is about a mouse, Mrs. Frisby. A widow with four children, Mrs. Frisby faces a terrible problem. Each year, she must move her children from their winter home in the farmer's field to their summer home. She must move before the farmer plows. This year, her youngest son is very sick. He cannot be moved.

One day Mrs. Frisby helps a crow escape from the farmer's cat. She asks the crow for help, and he suggests talking to the owl. Fearful but determined, she agrees. The owl tells her, "Go to the rats."

Although Mrs. Frisby is frightened, she finds the rats in their underground home. They can read, write, and solve problems! Their home has electricity, run on power stolen from the farmer. Their food comes from the farmer's garden. The rats agree to use their technical skill to help Mrs. Frisby.

5. What do you think happens next in the story?

Ⓐ The rats capture Mrs. Frisby.

Ⓑ The rats talk the farmer into moving his fields.

Ⓒ The rats help Mrs. Frisby and her children find safety.

Ⓓ Mrs. Frisby becomes too frightened to let the rats help her.

6. If her son hadn't been sick, Mrs. Frisby probably would have

Ⓐ moved to her summer home.

Ⓑ stayed longer in her winter house.

Ⓒ told the rats to leave her alone.

Ⓓ never seen a crow or an owl.

7. If the rats tell Mrs. Frisby that she will have to do something dangerous to help her son, she will probably

Ⓐ complain and stomp off.

Ⓑ refuse to do it.

Ⓒ gather her courage and complete the task.

Ⓓ ask her children to do it.

8. What will the farmer probably do when he learns the rats live on his farm?

Ⓐ welcome them to his farm

Ⓑ tell the cat to leave them alone

Ⓒ try to get rid of them

Ⓓ offer them more food and seeds

Read this news story about a stolen vase. Then answer the questions.

The Daily News   **January 12, 2002**

Caught Offguard!

Last night, Martin Collins was standing guard in the lobby of Center Theater. He had been hired by the theater owners to protect a priceless Mayan vase. The small vase was on display for the concert.

Collins saw a blond woman in a dark suit walk out of the concert and down the hall toward the ladies' room. Then he heard a loud scream.

As he gazed down the hall, a woman walked toward him. She had short, dark hair. She wore a bright-blue blouse and a black skirt. Her face looked familiar. He asked if she had heard the scream. She pointed toward the rear doors at the end of the hall. Torn between doing his job and helping someone, Collins glanced back. No one was around. The woman he had spoken to seemed about to enter the concert hall. Yet her head was turned toward the front doors.

Collins ran to the rear doors and found a blond wig and a black suit jacket. He raced back to the lobby. The vase was gone. At that moment, people poured out of the concert. Collins ran out the front doors.

9. Predict what probably happened next.

   Ⓐ Collins stopped everyone exiting the concert to question them.

   Ⓑ Collins looked outside for a woman with short, dark hair.

   Ⓒ Collins ran after a dark-haired man.

   Ⓓ Collins ran back to the rear doors at the end of the hallway.

10. If Collins had not run to the rear doors, what would have probably happened?

   Ⓐ Several concert goers would have stolen the vase.

   Ⓑ The vase would not have been stolen.

   Ⓒ The theater owners would have been angry with him.

   Ⓓ The concert would have ended sooner.

11. The police caught the thief within five minutes. Predict what the thief was wearing.

   Ⓐ a black suit

   Ⓑ a guard's uniform

   Ⓒ a blue blouse and a black skirt

   Ⓓ a Mayan costume

12. What will most likely happen to Collins now?

   Ⓐ He will be thanked by the theater owners for his good work at saving a person in trouble.

   Ⓑ The theater owners will express their disappointment with him and warn him to be more alert.

   Ⓒ He will meet the thief and help her sell the vase for a huge profit.

   Ⓓ He will never try to help anyone in trouble again.

PART FOUR: Prepare for a Test

▶ A test question about making a prediction may ask you to make a good guess about what will happen next in a reading passage, or what might happen in the future.

▶ A test question about making a prediction usually contains the words *predict*, *probably*, or *most likely*.

Here is a report on a science experiment. Read the report. Then do Numbers 13 and 14.

My experiment was on the shape and volume of liquids. First, I gathered this equipment: one graduated cylinder (or measuring cup)
three glass jars, each of a different shape
a pitcher of water

I marked each glass jar with a letter. The first jar was marked *A*, the second *B*, and the third *C*. I poured 100 mL of water from the pitcher into the graduated cylinder. Then I poured the water into jar A. I noted the height of the water in the jar. I marked the height with tape. Then I poured the water back into the cylinder. I noted how much water I had. The volume was 100 mL. This was the same volume as when I started.

I did the same steps for jar B. This was a short, wide jar. The water level was much lower than in jar A. But when I poured the water back into the cylinder, the volume was still 100 mL.

Last, I poured 100 mL of water into jar C. The height of the water was not as high as in jar A. It was higher than in jar B. Then I poured the water back into the cylinder.

Making Predictions

13. How much water will the student report was poured back from jar C?

    Ⓐ 50 mL
    Ⓑ 100 mL
    Ⓒ less than jar A and more than jar B
    Ⓓ more than jar A and less than jar B

Making Predictions

14. Predict what would happen if the student poured the water into a glass jar that was shorter and wider than jar B.

    Ⓐ The water would rise as high as it did in jar A.
    Ⓑ The water level would be lower than in jar B.
    Ⓒ The water level would be even with that of jar C.
    Ⓓ The water would be less than 100 mL when the student poured it back into the cylinder.

Here is a short biography of explorer Robert Peary. Read the biography. Then do Numbers 15 and 16.

Close Enough!

Robert Peary was born in 1856. As he grew, explorers opened many wild lands of North America. Yet the North Pole stayed unknown.

Peary dreamed of being a great explorer. He began with two trips to Greenland. He made maps of the region. But Peary longed to do something to get everyone's attention.

Peary decided to head for the North Pole. He tried twice. One trip was from 1898 to 1902. The other was from 1905 to 1906. Each trip was a failure.

In 1909, Peary set out for the North Pole again. He had four Inuit guides. His assistant was Matthew Henson. For thirty-six days the party traveled over the icy land. Finally, they reached the North Pole, or very near it. They sunk their flags into the snow.

Before the group returned home, there was trouble. An explorer named Frederick Cook claimed to have reached the North Pole a year before Peary. Experts checked Cook's records. They did not believe him.

Then Peary's claim came into doubt. Some important papers from his trip were missing. At last, the National Geographic Society and Congress agreed that Peary, along with Matthew Henson, had reached his mark—or close enough. Peary became a hero. But Cook did not give up.

Making Predictions

15. If the biography continued, what information would it most likely include?

  Ⓐ why Peary wasn't satisfied with exploring Greenland
  Ⓑ who officially recognized Peary's achievement
  Ⓒ how Cook tried again to get his claim accepted
  Ⓓ what Peary said when he reached the North Pole

Making Predictions

16. Predict what would have happened if Peary had been easily discouraged.

  Ⓐ He would have tried to reach the North Pole on his first trip.
  Ⓑ He would have given up after his first failed trip to the North Pole.
  Ⓒ He would have believed Cook's claims.
  Ⓓ He would have taken a longer route to the North Pole.

4-6 Review

PART ONE: Read a Myth

Here is a myth about how some helpful garden animals came to be.
Read the myth. Then do Numbers 1 through 6.

Earthworms, Butterflies, and Ladybugs

Long ago, Lea and her sister Ani lived on an island with lovely gray mountains and golden beaches. But there were no plants. No beautiful insects flew in the air, and nothing lived in the ground. Because the land lacked plants, the sisters decided to plant a garden. They asked their mother for seeds, and she gave them many types.

The sisters worked side-by-side preparing the soil, planting the seeds, and tending the plants. Lea worked patiently. Ani was also careful, but she often lost her temper.

One time, Lea pulled up a plant and bits of root dropped off. "You have ruined the plant," Ani complained, and she frowned at her sister.

"No, look. The root bits are turning into earthworms!" Lea pointed out smiling. "Earthworms are good for the soil."

The next day, while Lea worked, she sneezed because a light breeze tickled her nose. "Stop sneezing or you'll ruin the plants," Ani complained. Lea sneezed on a flower, and the petals flew off in all directions. "See! I told you," Ani said.

"No, look! The petals have turned into beautiful butterflies. They help flowers grow."

The next day, Lea held a handful of seeds that were round and red with black dots. "Don't drop any," Ani ordered. Suddenly, a strong wind blew.

Recognizing Cause and Effect

1. What caused the petals to fall off the flower?

   Ⓐ Ani knocked them off as she worked.
   Ⓑ Lea sneezed on the flower.
   Ⓒ Ani shook the flower.
   Ⓓ Lea pulled the plant up by the roots.

Comparing and Contrasting

4. How were the earthworms and the butterflies alike?

   Ⓐ Both were created by Lea's actions.
   Ⓑ Both came from across the seas to the island.
   Ⓒ Both grew from the roots planted in the garden.
   Ⓓ Both were ways Ani got back at her sister.

Recognizing Cause and Effect

2. Because the land had no plants, the sisters

   Ⓐ created earthworms and butterflies to help plants grow.
   Ⓑ asked their mother to work in the garden.
   Ⓒ decided to plant a garden.
   Ⓓ asked their mother for advice.

Making Predictions

5. What will most likely happen next?

   Ⓐ The wind will blow the seeds from Lea's hand.
   Ⓑ Ani will knock the seeds from Lea's hand.
   Ⓒ Lea will order her sister to be quiet.
   Ⓓ The seeds will turn into more earthworms and butterflies.

Comparing and Contrasting

3. How were Lea and Ani different?

   Ⓐ Lea worked hard in the garden, but Ani was lazy.
   Ⓑ Lea dared to ask her mother for seeds, but Ani was afraid.
   Ⓒ Lea liked gardening, but gardening made Ani unhappy.
   Ⓓ Lea saw good things come from mistakes, but Ani thought mistakes ruined everything.

Making Predictions

6. Whenever Lea makes a mistake, it is likely that Ani will

   Ⓐ help her correct it.
   Ⓑ scold her for her mistake.
   Ⓒ go off and tell their mother.
   Ⓓ tell Lea not to worry.

Here is a journal entry written long ago by a teenager in Norway.
Read the journal entry. Then do Numbers 7 through 12.

January 12, 1923

    Yesterday and all last night it snowed so much that the ground was thickly covered. I arose before my parents and my sister Lucia, and rubbed away the ice on the window with my warm hand. I saw the morning sun rise in a golden glow, and every sparkling flake looked magical. I longed to go out skiing with the new wooden skis Father had just given me. So I dressed and rushed to the kitchen, leaving Lucia sound asleep in her room as usual.

    Father and Mother were stirring in the bedroom. "Peter," Mother yelled to me, "I'll make breakfast. You need to go out this morning, right away."

    I was surprised Mother knew what I was thinking. Perhaps she just knew me and how I love skiing. But I wondered why she said *need*, not *want*.

    Mother came out in her dressing gown and put more wood on the fire in the stove. She cooked some cereal for me. Then she gave me the news.

    She said I would have to travel to the cottage we kept by the lake. Grandmother and Grandfather had gone there for a few days, but all the snow would be too much for them to shovel. That meant no skiing for me and a long hard hike on snowshoes. Though I was disappointed, I knew I had to help my grandparents.

Recognizing Cause and Effect

7. Peter rubbed away the ice on the window because

    Ⓐ he wanted to see outside.
    Ⓑ the window was dirty on the inside.
    Ⓒ he wanted to break the glass.
    Ⓓ he wanted to warm his hands.

Recognizing Cause and Effect

8. What is an effect of the snowstorm?

    Ⓐ Peter's grandparents can't get to the cottage without help.
    Ⓑ Peter will be able to ski all day.
    Ⓒ Peter's parents send him to help his grandparents.
    Ⓓ Peter must hike through the snow and carry home his grandparents.

Comparing and Contrasting

9. In the journal entry, how is Peter different from his sister?

    Ⓐ He likes snow.
    Ⓑ He gets up earlier.
    Ⓒ He is older.
    Ⓓ He is more helpful.

Comparing and Contrasting

10. How do Peter's feelings change in the journal entry?

    Ⓐ from annoyed to excited
    Ⓑ from happy to angry
    Ⓒ from excited to disappointed
    Ⓓ from discouraged to cheerful

Making Predictions

11. What do you think Peter's journal entry for the next day will discuss?

    Ⓐ what he saw and did as he hiked to the cottage and helped his grandparents
    Ⓑ how he hurried to the cottage, shoveled out his grandparents, ran home, and skied all afternoon
    Ⓒ how Lucia and his parents met him at the cottage with food
    Ⓓ how the storm began after he left and he got lost in the snow

Making Predictions

12. Predict what Peter's grandparents will say when he arrives.

    Ⓐ "We were expecting the whole family, but sit down and have some tea."
    Ⓑ "Did you come to skate?"
    Ⓒ "We're happy you are here to help clear snow from the cottage."
    Ⓓ "We are starving. Did you bring any food?"

Finding Word Meaning in Context

PART ONE: Learn About Finding Word Meaning in Context

Read this paragraph about gymnast Nadia Comaneci. The word *astounded* appears in the fourth sentence. As you read, use the underlined word and phrase as clues to help you figure out the meaning of the word *astounded*.

It was the summer of 1976, at the Olympic Games. A young Romanian gymnast walked to the balance beam. Her name was Nadia. As she lifted her body in <u>amazing</u> twists and leaps, she astounded the audience. They <u>could not believe their eyes</u>! Surely, this young athlete was bringing her sport to a new height.

You can figure out the meaning of the word *astounded* by looking at the words and phrases around it. The word *amazing* and the phrase *could not believe their eyes* are clues to the meaning of the word *astounded*.

The meaning of the word *astounded* is "amazed or astonished."

When you use clues in a reading passage to figure out the meaning of a new word, you are **finding word meaning in context**. The words and phrases around a new word often provide clues to the word's meaning. These clues are called **context clues**.

▶ Context clues are often in the sentence where the new word appears. They can also be in sentences before and after the word.

▶ Clues about the meaning of a new word are often found by thinking about the way the word is used in the sentence.

▶ Clues about the meaning of a new word can be found by thinking about the facts and details in the paragraph where the word is found.

Read this article about Pawnee drums. As you read the last paragraph, ask yourself, "What clues will I use to figure out the meaning of the word *utensil?*" Then answer the questions.

Many Pawnee follow the old way for making drums. The drum maker cuts a strip of board about 3 inches wide and 64 inches long. He trims the board to about $\frac{1}{3}$ inch thick. Next, the drum maker drills holes near the ends. Using boiling water and steam, he treats the wood so it bends. He laces the two ends of the board together to form a circle frame.

The head of the drum is made of a round piece of animal hide, about 20 inches across. Working with a sharp bone utensil, the drum maker uses the instrument to punch holes along the edge of the hide. Then he wets the hide and stretches it over the frame. He loops wet rawhide laces through the holes in the hide and ties them together at the center of the back so they can be tightened. As the hide and laces dry, both shrink and grow tight. Finally, he paints the drum.

Front of Pawnee drum

Back of Pawnee drum

1. In the last paragraph, the word *utensil* probably means

   Ⓐ "a spoon."
   Ⓑ "a tool."
   Ⓒ "a machine."
   Ⓓ "a frame."

2. Which word gives a clue to the meaning of the word *utensil?*

   Ⓐ instrument
   Ⓑ sharp
   Ⓒ hide
   Ⓓ loops

Work with a partner. Talk about your answers to questions 1 and 2. Tell why you chose the answers you did.

PART TWO: Check Your Understanding

Remember: The words and phrases around a new word often give clues to the word's meaning.

▶ Look for context clues in the sentence where the new word appears. Look also in the sentences before and after the new word.

▶ Look for clues about the meaning of a new word by thinking about the way the new word is used in the sentence.

▶ Look for clues about the meaning of a new word by thinking about the facts and details in the paragraph where the new word is found.

Read this short biography of Thurgood Marshall. As you read, think about how you will figure out the meaning of any new words. Then answer the questions.

In 1933, Thurgood Marshall began a career in law. At the same time, he worked for human rights.

In 1954, Marshall argued his most important legal case. The results would affect the country's future. They would change education. At that time, black children and white children were isolated from each other. They had to go to separate schools. The question Marshall argued was "Is this against the laws of the United States?"

Marshall believed it was. He felt public schools should teach blacks and whites equally and together. After months of effort, Marshall won his case.

Over the years, Marshall's fame grew. He became a member of the Supreme Court. He was the first African-American to be chosen for the court. In this role, he kept working for the rights of all Americans.

Thurgood Marshall, just before being sworn in as a member of the Supreme Court in 1967

3. What is the meaning of the word *isolated* in paragraph two?

Ⓐ "kept apart"
Ⓑ "taught the same lessons"
Ⓒ "grouped together"
Ⓓ "sent home from school"

4. Which phrase gives a clue to the meaning of the word *isolated*?

Ⓐ his most important legal case
Ⓑ had to go to separate schools
Ⓒ believed it was
Ⓓ affect the country's future

Look at the answer choices for each question.
Read why each answer choice is correct or not correct.

3. What is the meaning of the word *isolated* in paragraph two?

   ● "kept apart"
   This answer is correct because, in the biography, the words and phrases around the word isolated *state that black children and white children had to go to separate schools. You can find meaning in context to figure out that* isolated *means "kept apart."*

   Ⓑ "taught the same lessons"
   This answer is not correct because nothing in the biography suggests whether or not the students were taught the same lessons.

   Ⓒ "grouped together"
   This answer is not correct because it is the opposite of what the biography states. Black children and white children could not be grouped together if they had to go to separate schools.

   Ⓓ "sent home from school"
   This answer is not correct because the biography suggests nothing about anyone being sent home from school.

4. Which phrase gives a clue to the meaning of the word *isolated*?

   Ⓐ his most important legal case
   This answer is not correct because it tells something about Thurgood Marshall. This detail gives no information about the children or why they were isolated.

   ● had to go to separate schools
   This answer is correct because it tells what the word isolated *means. It connects the idea of black children and white children being isolated by attending separate schools.*

   Ⓒ believed it was
   This answer is not correct because it tells how Marshall felt about the law, but it does not further explain the word isolated.

   Ⓓ affect the country's future
   This answer is not correct because it does not provide any information that helps define the word isolated.

PART THREE: Learn More About Finding Word Meaning in Context

▶ Look for a synonym, a word with a similar meaning, near a new word in a reading passage.

▶ Look for an antonym, a word with an opposite meaning, near a new word in a reading passage.

▶ Once you think you know the meaning of a new word, read the sentence where the word appears, using this new meaning. Does the sentence still make sense? If so, you've probably figured out the meaning of the new word.

> **Read this travel brochure about Europe's landforms. Then answer the questions.**

Europe is a small continent filled with a variety of landforms. These different types of land features attract visitors with their beauty.

Along the north coast of Europe is a plain of flat and rolling land. The eastern part of the plain is wide. The western part is narrow. Many of Europe's largest cities lie on this narrow plain.

Seaports rest near the coast at the mouth of rivers. The city of Hamburg sits near where the Elbe River enters the North Sea. The city of Gdansk lies at the mouth of the Vistula River.

River valleys make good farmland. The Rhine River has a large plain that is lush. Farmers need rich land like this to grow food crops.

In the center of Europe are low hills and mountains. On these lands, farmers raise livestock, such as sheep and goats. Also, Europe has lovely snow-covered mountains. The Alps are most applauded. Nearly everyone has heard of them. The Alps and other mountains make Europe a favorite for winter sports.

5. In paragraph one, which words give a clue to the meaning of *variety*?

Ⓐ small continent   Ⓒ land features
Ⓑ attract visitors   Ⓓ different types

6. Which definition of the word *mouth* is used in paragraph three?

Ⓐ "the lips on the human face"
Ⓑ "the opening through which a container is filled"
Ⓒ "the place where a river empties into the sea"
Ⓓ "the opening in a flute's mouthpiece"

7. In paragraph four, which clue word is a synonym of *lush*?

Ⓐ river   Ⓒ rich
Ⓑ large   Ⓓ food

8. In the last paragraph, you can tell that the word *applauded* means

Ⓐ "popular."
Ⓑ "praised."
Ⓒ "unknown."
Ⓓ "disliked."

Whitefoot the Wise

"Whitefoot, Whitefoot," I called all afternoon. My cat's name is Whitefoot because she has big white paws. The rest of her body is sooty black. She is a special cat who seems to know what I am thinking. She also is shrewd. In fact, Whitefoot is so clever that I couldn't believe it when she failed to come home. Where could she be?

Dad and I went outside later and called for her. At night, wise Whitefoot usually comes right away, but not this time. We didn't even hear the tap of her feet on the hard ground or a rustle in the grass. Instead of hope, I felt despair. Neighbors had counseled us to keep her inside, but we didn't listen to their warning. Had we made a terrible mistake?

Coyotes had appeared lately in people's yards. One cat had disappeared. I didn't want that to happen to Whitefoot!

Dad suggested we go outside once more. That's when I saw a stealthy shadow sneak out of our yard. Suddenly, I heard a scratching of tree bark, and I saw four white feet edging down a tree trunk. Whitefoot! Was the shadow a coyote or another danger? We will never know. But Whitefoot does!

9. In paragraph one, which clue word is a synonym of *shrewd*?

  Ⓐ tiny
  Ⓑ special
  Ⓒ clever
  Ⓓ sooty

10. In paragraph two, which clue word is an antonym of *despair*?

  Ⓐ wise
  Ⓑ time
  Ⓒ hope
  Ⓓ terrible

11. In paragraph two, the best meaning of the word *counseled* is

  Ⓐ "ordered."
  Ⓑ "asked."
  Ⓒ "advised."
  Ⓓ "threatened."

12. In the last paragraph, the word *stealthy* means

  Ⓐ "strange."
  Ⓑ "black."
  Ⓒ "quiet."
  Ⓓ "noisy."

▶ A test question about finding word meaning in context asks you about the meaning of a word from a reading passage. The word may or may not be familiar to you. The word might also be used in a new way.

▶ A test question about finding word meaning in context usually has several answer choices. Try each answer choice in the sentence in which the word appears. Decide which answer choice makes the most sense in the reading passage.

Here is part of a question and answer column from a newspaper.
Read part of the column. Then do Numbers 13 and 14.

Question: My name is Alex. I want to know if I can name a hill in my town.

Answer: Yes, Alex, you can. But take the right steps. The United States Board of Geographic Names will decide about the name you choose. They will ask you questions. You need to have the right answers.

First, make sure that the hill is not already named. Do not name it after a living person. Choose your name carefully. A humorous name will not be put on a map. The government wants only serious names on its official maps.

Next, visit the government website listed at the end of this column. Fill out the form. The form asks you to describe the land. You must also locate the hill exactly. Finally, you must defend the name you want, so give a good reason for choosing it. In several months, the Board will tell you what they decide. They may accept a name you pick, such as Cactus Hill or Great Fox Run.

Finding Word Meaning in Context

13. In the second paragraph of the answer, the word *humorous* means

Ⓐ "serious."
Ⓑ "official."
Ⓒ "correct."
Ⓓ "amusing."

Finding Word Meaning in Context

14. In the last paragraph of the answer, the best meaning for the word *defend* is

Ⓐ "give support for an idea."
Ⓑ "give examples of."
Ⓒ "provide the exact location of."
Ⓓ "accept without question."

Here is an article about changing the weather. Read the article. Then do Numbers 15 and 16.

It's raining, and you have a big soccer game. You're a skier, and it's too warm for snow. What can you do?

People often say you cannot change the weather. But it might be better to say that you cannot change the weather without consequences. There can be unexpected results to any change. This must also be true for weather changes.

Pier destroyed by a hurricane

In the 1970s, the United States had a weather project called Stormfury. The plan was to weaken hurricanes. These storms have heavy winds and rains. Lowering the speed of the winds even a little could prevent much damage. The eastern coast of the United States would be protected.

Stormfury pilots flew out on eight different days. Their job was to "attack" four hurricanes with a special chemical. The chemical was supposed to make the eye of the hurricane larger. If this happened, the winds would slow. On half of the days, nothing happened. But on the rest of the days, the winds of the hurricane slackened. That was a good result!

In the 1980s, some weather experts claimed that the weakened hurricanes were not because of Stormfury. They said that the hurricanes changed naturally. However, other experts claimed a different result. They said that Stormfury worked too well, and had prevented rain from reaching Mexico. A severe drought was blamed on the program. Could Stormfury really have caused the dry weather? No one is certain, but the program was halted.

Finding Word Meaning in Context

15. What is the best meaning of the word *consequences* in paragraph two?

   Ⓐ "causes"
   Ⓑ "results"
   Ⓒ "reasons"
   Ⓓ "changes"

Finding Word Meaning in Context

16. The most likely meaning of the word *slackened* in paragraph four is

   Ⓐ "grew less strong."
   Ⓑ "became more damaging."
   Ⓒ "stopped completely."
   Ⓓ "caused minor damage."

Drawing Conclusions and Making Inferences

PART ONE: Learn About Drawing Conclusions
and Making Inferences

Read this story about Michelle. The story does not tell you what she is wearing to protect herself. As you read, use the underlined sentences as clues to help you figure out what Michelle is wearing for protection.

Head First

Michelle started down the hill, twisting her body to keep the snowboard in control. She glanced at the other snowboarders. <u>They were all wearing safety helmets.</u>

Suddenly, Michelle's snowboard hit an icy patch and she spilled. With a thud, her head hit the icy hill. She sat up dazed but fine. <u>She patted her head and thought, "I could have gotten hurt without this."</u>

The story does not tell you that Michelle wore a helmet. It does, however, give details that help you figure this out on your own.

They were all wearing safety helmets.

She patted her head and thought, "I could have gotten hurt without this."

These details help you figure out that Michelle is wearing a helmet. You probably know from your own experience that wearing a helmet helps prevent serious injuries in many kinds of sports and other activities.

Details are sometimes not stated or explained in a reading passage. You must figure out some information on your own. Whenever you figure out something that is not told in a reading passage, you are **drawing a conclusion or making an inference.**

▶ Pay attention to the details in a reading passage. You can use these details to figure out information that is not stated or explained.

▶ Use the details from the reading passage, as well as what you know from your own life, to draw a conclusion or make an inference.

Read about recycling in this letter to the editor. As you read, look for details to help you figure out how the writer feels. Then answer the questions.

Dear Editor:

Our town started its recycling program five years ago. I felt hopeful. What a help it is to be able to put items that can be recycled into a bin and have them picked up in front of our homes. What a chance to help the earth! After two years, the town sent out a list of a few things that could no longer be recycled. It was a short list. I should have seen it as a warning.

Last week, the list of things that could not be recycled grew longer. Now we can't recycle plastic bags, for example. Even though plastic can be recycled, the town says that plastic bags blow out of the recycle bins, making a mess. Well, I'm sure they make a mess in landfills, too! Isn't our town's recycling program heading in the wrong direction?

A Worried Citizen

1. You can tell that the writer of the letter feels that

Ⓐ people are not doing their part in recycling.

Ⓑ picking up items in front of homes for recycling isn't working.

Ⓒ the town should recycle more items, not fewer.

Ⓓ plastic bags belong in landfills.

2. Which detail from the letter helped you answer question 1?

Ⓐ Our town started its recycling program five years ago.

Ⓑ I felt hopeful.

Ⓒ It was a short list.

Ⓓ Isn't our town's recycling program heading in the wrong direction?

Work with a partner. Talk about your answers to questions 1 and 2. Tell why you chose the answers you did.

PART TWO: Check Your Understanding

Remember: **Drawing a conclusion or making an inference is a way of figuring out information that is not stated in a reading passage.**

▶ Think about the details that are stated in a reading passage. Use these details to figure out information that is not explained.

▶ Use the details from the reading passage and what you know from your own life to draw a conclusion or make an inference.

Read this diary entry. As you read, ask yourself, "What details are explained? What information can I figure out on my own?" Then answer the questions.

When I woke this morning, the sun drew me to the window. The last bit of snow had finally melted along the edge of the driveway. Now there was a ridge of sand where the snow had been.

The sun was shining on our field of white flowers. They are always the first every year to bloom. Each flower looked like a tiny lantern. The field seemed magical. Grabbing a jacket, I hurried out the door. Mom usually makes me eat breakfast before I go outside. Since Mom was visiting Aunt Becky, I could eat when I came back inside.

It was much warmer outside than I expected. As I walked through the flowers, I startled a snake. It stopped a few feet away, holding its foot-long body perfectly still with its head high. I could see a yellow diamond pattern on its belly, but its back was mostly black with tiny, almost blue squares. Three gold stripes ran from head to tip. I could have stood and watched it forever, but it slipped into the flowery grasses. Perhaps I'll find its picture in a snake book someday so I can discover what kind it was. For today, seeing the snake was enough.

3. From the diary entry, what can you tell about the season?

Ⓐ It is the middle of winter.
Ⓑ It is early spring.
Ⓒ It is the warmest part of summer.
Ⓓ It is late fall.

4. From the diary entry, you can conclude that the writer

Ⓐ was worried because her mother was not home.
Ⓑ knew what kind of snake she saw.
Ⓒ is afraid of snakes.
Ⓓ finds snakes interesting.

Look at the answer choices for each question.
Read why each answer choice is correct or not correct.

3. From the diary entry, what can you tell about the season?

   Ⓐ It is the middle of winter.
   This answer is not correct because the writer states that the last snow had finally melted. This suggests winter has ended.

   ● It is early spring.
   This answer is correct because it fits the details of the diary entry. The last snow has melted, but sand is still at the side of the driveway where the snow had been. The first flowers are blooming. The writer takes a jacket to go outside. From these facts, you can conclude it is the start of spring.

   Ⓒ It is the warmest part of summer.
   This answer is not correct because the details in the diary entry all suggest that it is spring. The day is warm, but the writer tells you that the heat is unexpected.

   Ⓓ It is late fall.
   This answer is not correct because there are no details about fall in the diary entry.

4. From the diary entry, you can conclude that the writer

   Ⓐ was worried because her mother was not home.
   This answer is not correct because there are no details that suggest the writer was worried because her mother was not home. The writer seemed pleased that she could go outside before eating breakfast.

   Ⓑ knew what kind of snake she saw.
   This answer is not correct because the diary entry reveals the writer did not know the kind of snake she saw. She hopes to find its picture in a book someday.

   Ⓒ is afraid of snakes.
   This answer is not correct because the writer would not have stayed and studied the snake, nor wished to watch it forever, if she was afraid of snakes.

   ● finds snakes interesting.
   This answer is correct because the way the writer acted shows strong interest. She watched the snake carefully and studied its markings until the snake slithered away. She hopes to identify the snake someday.

PART THREE: Learn More About Drawing Conclusions and Making Inferences

▶ Look for details in a reading passage that tell how a person or character looks, acts, thinks, feels, and speaks. Think about what you know about people with similar qualities.

▶ Look for details in a reading passage that suggest where or when something happens. If something happens at the Grand Canyon, you know that events are taking place in the United States. If something happens while the sun is shining, you know that events are taking place during the daytime.

Read this report about a star pattern. Then answer the questions.

Greek Myths in the Sky

Orion is a well-known star pattern, or constellation. From December to March, Orion is easy to find because that is when it is high and bright in the sky.

Orion is a character in many Greek myths. Orion was a great hunter. He often bragged, "No animal can escape me." The gods became angry. They sent a poisonous spider to bite him. After Orion died, the gods placed him in the sky.

In the sky behind Orion are his two faithful dogs. They are Canis Major and Canis Minor. *Canis* means "dog." Under Orion's foot is the small, faint constellation of Lepus. *Lepus* is another word for *hare*. Lepus is low on the horizon. He seems to be hiding from Orion. In Greek myths, Lepus hid or ran from the great hunter.

5. Details in the report suggest that the constellation Orion

   Ⓐ is harder to find from April to November.
   Ⓑ has more stars than any other constellation.
   Ⓒ is alone in the night sky.
   Ⓓ has the brightest stars.

6. From the report, you can tell that the character Orion

   Ⓐ was very shy.
   Ⓑ became a brave warrior.
   Ⓒ was proud of his hunting skills.
   Ⓓ knew a lot about stars.

7. From the report, you can conclude that the gods

   Ⓐ never liked Orion.
   Ⓑ did not enjoy Orion's bragging.
   Ⓒ were better hunters than Orion.
   Ⓓ wanted Orion to kill the spider.

8. You can tell that the constellation Lepus appears

   Ⓐ about to attack Orion's foot.
   Ⓑ bold with bright stars.
   Ⓒ afraid of Orion.
   Ⓓ high above the horizon.

Read this story about two boys at the beach. Then answer the questions.

High Wind Warning

"Hey, Tim, I want to fly my kite," Jackson said.

Tim looked kindly at his younger cousin. He said, "Look at the weather forecast posted on the board. It says, 'high wind warning.' "

"Yes, but that's just for swimmers because the surf is high. I want to fly my kite today," Jackson stomped, kicking sand into the air.

"Listen, Mom and Aunt Ellie left me in charge. I agreed to come out to the beach with you and check the weather. But it's not safe to fly the kite," Tim said firmly.

Even as Tim spoke, Jackson pulled the kite from the kite bag and tossed it into the air. He let the string unwind. The kite lifted high and the wind grabbed it so strongly that Jackson was being pulled along the beach.

"Help me! Help me! I'll be blown away," Jackson yelled. Tim ran after his cousin and grabbed the line.

"Will you listen to me now?" Tim asked. But Jackson was too shaken to speak. He just nodded his head.

9. From the story, what can you tell about Jackson?

Ⓐ He is very shy.

Ⓑ He always does what is right.

Ⓒ He is stubborn.

Ⓓ He cannot read signs.

10. When Tim says, "But it's not safe to fly the kite," you can conclude that Tim

Ⓐ never thinks it's safe to fly a kite.

Ⓑ doesn't expect Jackson to disobey him.

Ⓒ takes his responsibility for his cousin seriously.

Ⓓ doesn't like kite flying.

11. At the end of the story, you can conclude that Jackson is

Ⓐ sneaky.

Ⓑ sad.

Ⓒ mean.

Ⓓ afraid.

12. From the ending of the story, you can tell that

Ⓐ the boys have one day left at the beach.

Ⓑ Jackson will obey his cousin in the future.

Ⓒ the wind is about to change.

Ⓓ many people are walking along the crowded beach.

➡️ A test question about drawing conclusions or making inferences asks you to figure out something that is not stated in a reading passage.

➡️ A test question about drawing conclusions or making inferences often contains the words *you can tell*, *determine*, or *conclude*.

Here is a science article about water. Read the article.
Then do Numbers 13 and 14.

Going Up! Going Down!

The movement of water is among the most pleasing sights in nature. Ocean tides flow in and out. Streams bubble over rocks. Rain dances as it splashes to the ground. Sometimes, the power and force of water can be fascinating to observe.

In some places beneath the earth, hot rock heats water that has seeped into the ground. The water grows hot enough to boil and turn to steam. When enough steam forms, the pressure builds. Then a geyser may shoot out of the ground. It can go a few feet high or up to 1,500 feet. Yellowstone Park is one place that is famous for its geysers. Yellowstone's highest geyser, Steamboat, reaches about 380 feet.

In a waterfall, water at one level drops to another level. Angel Falls in Venezuela is the highest falls in the world. The water crashes 3,212 feet over Devil's Mountain. Niagara Falls, on the border of the United States and Canada, is a wide falls. But the widest falls in the world is Khône Falls in Laos. Its width is 6.7 miles. Its longest drop is just 70 feet.

Niagara Falls

Drawing Conclusions and Making Inferences

13. You can tell that geysers can be found
   Ⓐ only in Yellowstone Park.
   Ⓑ where waterfalls also form.
   Ⓒ near bubbling streams.
   Ⓓ where water heats under the ground.

Drawing Conclusions and Making Inferences

14. There is enough information in the article to determine that waterfalls
   Ⓐ need level land.
   Ⓑ always form near an ocean.
   Ⓒ begin and end at two different heights.
   Ⓓ can be high or wide, but not both.

Here is a report on a scene from *The Lord of the Rings* by J.R.R. Tolkien.
Read the report. Then do Numbers 15 and 16.

The most magical part of the book *The Lord of the Rings* is when Frodo
Baggins meets Lady Galadriel in her house in the land of the elves. Frodo is the
bearer of a powerful ring. He must guard the ring with his life until he reaches
the one place where it can be destroyed.

Frodo has been traveling with eight other beings. Three beings are hobbits
like him. Two are men. One is a dwarf. One is an elf. The last one is a
good sorcerer who has just fallen into a deep hole during a fight with an evil
monster called a Balrog.

Frodo and the seven remaining travelers have entered a light-filled land
where only elves live. The beautiful Lady Galadriel is a ruler here. She takes
Frodo to look into a pool of water, her magic mirror. In it, he sees scenes of the
past, the present, and the future, all mixing together.

The power of the woman causes him to offer her the ring, even though he
has been guarding it with his life. But Lady Galadriel decides not to take it even
though she knows the ring could bring her great power. She also knows that
whatever happens with the ring, the life of her people will change. She sends
Frodo off to continue his journey to destroy the ring.

Drawing Conclusions and Making Inferences

15. From the report, you can tell that Lady Galadriel is

    Ⓐ an unkind woman.
    Ⓑ a wise and fair elf.
    Ⓒ evil and self-centered.
    Ⓓ not interested in jewelry.

Drawing Conclusions and Making Inferences

16. From the report, what can you conclude about the trip Frodo is making?

    Ⓐ He is on a pleasant vacation.
    Ⓑ The trip is dangerous and important.
    Ⓒ The trip began in the land of the elves.
    Ⓓ He is returning home.

Distinguishing Between Fact and Opinion

PART ONE: Learn About Distinguishing Between Fact and Opinion

Read this paragraph about Maria Martínez. The statements that can be proved are underlined. As you read, look for statements that tell what the writer thinks or feels.

Maria Martínez was the best potter ever. <u>She was a Tewa Indian.</u> <u>In 1908, Maria's husband was helping scientists dig ruins in a canyon.</u> <u>One of the scientists found a piece of an unusual black pot.</u> <u>He asked Maria if she could make a pot like that.</u> She was very clever. <u>She made a modern pot like the ancient one.</u> Maria's work was the most magnificent anyone had ever seen.

The statements that can be proved are
She was a Tewa Indian.
In 1908, Maria's husband was helping scientists dig ruins in a canyon.
One of the scientists found a piece of an unusual black pot.
He asked Maria if she could make a pot like that.
She made a modern pot like the ancient one.

The statements that tell what the writer thinks or feels are
Maria Martínez was the best potter ever.
She was very clever.
Maria's work was the most magnificent anyone had ever seen.

If a statement can be proved, it is a **fact**. If a statement tells what someone thinks or feels, it is an **opinion**. Opinions cannot be proved. When you figure out if a statement is a fact or an opinion, you are **distinguishing between fact and opinion**.

▶ Facts are statements that can be checked or proved.

▶ Opinions are statements that cannot be proved. They tell what someone thinks, feels, or believes.

▶ Opinions often contain clue words such as *think, feel, believe,* and *seem.* Other common clue words are *always, never, all, none, most, least, greatest, best,* and *worst.*

Read this essay. As you read, ask yourself, "Which statements can be proved? Which statements cannot be proved?" Then answer the questions.

Freedom

The United States is a free nation. Its flag is a symbol of freedom. The flag has 50 stars, one for each of the 50 states. It has 13 stripes, one for each of the original colonies.

Behind this symbol of freedom stand citizens, about 300 million. Some of these people work in the government. Some teach or provide other services. Some make goods.

These people help make the nation great. Everyone in the country benefits.

I am a part of this great nation. Yet, I am also one person. What does freedom mean to me?

Freedom is the most important quality of my life. Because I am free, I can choose my work. I can help decide who will be our next president. I can help make the best laws for the nation, the state, and my own community. I believe these are rights that no one should take away from me.

1. Which statement is a fact?

Ⓐ It has 13 stripes, one for each of the original colonies.

Ⓑ These people help make the nation great.

Ⓒ Everyone in the country benefits.

Ⓓ Freedom is the most important quality of my life.

2. Which clue word signals an opinion about making laws?

Ⓐ believe

Ⓑ important

Ⓒ best

Ⓓ great

Work with a partner. Talk about your answers to questions 1 and 2. Tell why you chose the answers you did.

Remember: Facts can be proved. Opinions cannot be proved.

▶ To find out if a statement is a fact, ask yourself, "Can this statement be proved?"

▶ To find out if a statement is an opinion, ask yourself, "Does this statement tell what someone thinks or feels?"

▶ Look for clue words that signal an opinion. Clue words include *think, feel, believe, seem, always, never, all, none, most, least, greatest, best,* and *worst.*

Read this article from a school newspaper that tells about a new club. As you read, think about which statements are facts and which statements are opinions. Then answer the questions.

Want a Challenge? Want Excitement? Join Us!

This spring, Blake Middle School will have a club for mountain bikers. Our teacher helpers are Miss Smith and Mr. Sanchez. We will be the first mountain biking club at school. Even if other clubs start up, ours will always be the best!

Right now, we want members. Join us! If you don't already mountain bike, it's easy to learn. We can help you. Mountain biking is great. You'll get lots of exercise, and have fun with friends.

Of course, you'll need a bike. You can learn about the features of mountain bikes from a book. Most important, get a bike with good tight shocks to handle the bumps.

Our uniform is flashy yellow and black. These are the best colors because we stand out from everyone else. State law requires that you wear a helmet. For more information, see me after school in Miss Smith's room. Soon you'll be having the most fun possible.

Kris "Rock Jumper" Morton

3. Which of these statements can be proved?

Ⓐ Even if other clubs start up, ours will always be the best!

Ⓑ If you don't already mountain bike, it's easy to learn.

Ⓒ State law requires that you wear a helmet.

Ⓓ Soon you'll be having the most fun possible!

4. Which of these statements tells what someone thinks or feels?

Ⓐ We will be the first mountain biking club at school.

Ⓑ Our teacher helpers are Miss Smith and Mr. Sanchez.

Ⓒ You can learn about the features of mountain bikes from a book.

Ⓓ These are the best colors because we stand out from everyone else.

Look at the answer choices for each question.
Read why each answer choice is correct or not correct.

3. Which of these statements can be proved?

   Ⓐ Even if other clubs start up, ours will always be the best!

   This answer is not correct because it cannot be proved that the mountain biking club will always be the best. The clue words always *and* best *signal that this statement is an opinion, not a fact.*

   Ⓑ If you don't already mountain bike, it's easy to learn.

   This answer is not correct because it cannot be proved that mountain biking is easy to learn. It may be easy for some people, but it may be difficult for others.

   ● State law requires that you wear a helmet.

   This answer is correct because you can prove that this statement is true. You can check the laws for the state to find out if there is a helmet law for mountain bikers.

   Ⓓ Soon you'll be having the most fun possible!

   This answer is not correct because it states an opinion that cannot be proved. No one can say whether being in the club will be the "most fun possible." For some people it may be, but for others it may not. The clue word most *signals that this statement is an opinion, not a fact.*

4. Which of these statements tells what someone thinks or feels?

   Ⓐ We will be the first mountain biking club at school.

   This answer is not correct because this statement is a fact that can be proved. You can check with the school to find out if another mountain biking club already exists.

   Ⓑ Our teacher helpers are Miss Smith and Mr. Sanchez.

   This answer is not correct because this statement can be proved. You can ask Miss Smith, Mr. Sanchez, or school officials if the teachers mentioned are in charge of the club.

   Ⓒ You can learn about the features of mountain bikes from a book.

   This answer is not correct because this statement is true and can be proved. You can find books about the features of mountain bikes in a library or in a book store.

   ● These are the best colors because we stand out from everyone else.

   This answer is correct because it states the writer's opinion about the uniform. It cannot be proved that the colors are the "best" or even that they make the bikers "stand out from everyone else." The clue word best *signals that this statement is an opinion, not a fact.*

PART THREE: Learn More About Distinguishing Between Fact and Opinion

▶ Facts can be observed, checked, or tested. You can prove that a fact is true.

▶ Opinions express someone's thoughts, feelings, or beliefs. An opinion can be about an event, an idea, a person, or a thing. Even though a person might agree or disagree with an opinion, it still cannot be proved.

> Read this article about numbers. Then answer the questions.

Lucky Numbers

Numbers can be written in word form, such as five. Numbers can also be written using a numeral, or number symbol. The symbol 5 is a numeral that means the same as five. Numbers are the easiest way to keep track of how many of a particular thing you have.

Using numbers helped people of the past record facts. Shopkeepers wrote the amount of goods ordered. There could never be any confusion when the order was filled.

Numbers are useful in many ways. But I believe numbers can also bring good luck. My lucky number is seven. I chose the number seven because it shows up in the most important places. For example, about seven days make up each phase of the moon. Seven notes make up the musical scale. Seven colors create a rainbow. There are even seven days in a week. I think the best day is Saturday, the seventh day. Seven is the greatest number. It has never failed to bring me luck!

---

5. Which of these is a fact from the article?

Ⓐ The symbol 5 is a numeral that means the same as five.

Ⓑ Numbers are the easiest way to keep track of how many of something we have.

Ⓒ I believe numbers can also bring good luck.

Ⓓ There could never be any confusion when the order was filled.

6. Which of these clue words signals an opinion the writer has about the days of the week?

Ⓐ believe   Ⓒ never

Ⓑ best   Ⓓ greatest

7. Which of these statements cannot be proved?

Ⓐ It has never failed to bring me luck.

Ⓑ Numbers are useful in many ways.

Ⓒ Seven notes make up the musical scale.

Ⓓ About seven days make up each phase of the moon.

8. A fact about the number seven that can be proved is

Ⓐ seven shows up in the most important places.

Ⓑ seven colors create a rainbow.

Ⓒ seven is the greatest number.

Ⓓ seven has never failed to bring the writer luck.

The Countess's Program

Today, lots of people write computer programs. They create the language that lets the computer work. Who wrote the first program?

You might think it was the man who designed the first computer. Charles Babbage was born in England in 1792. He planned two machines. The first machine was the difference engine. Babbage had a good idea. The machine would print math tables.

The second machine he planned was the analytical engine. It was the most important idea of the time. The machine was to be like today's computer. The idea showed how clever Babbage was. Although he never built it, everyone says he invented the computer. Babbage was a great inventor. But he did not write the program.

History is often unfair. You can find information about Babbage in many books. Yet, it is harder to find facts about the person who wrote the first program.

This person was Ada Byron Lovelace. She was a countess who lived in England. She was also Babbages's friend. She was great at math. She wrote the first program. She also wrote about uses for the computer. The United States Department of Defense recognized her work. They named the programming language Ada after her.

9. Which of these statements is a fact about Charles Babbage?

Ⓐ Babbage was clever.
Ⓑ Babbage was born in 1792.
Ⓒ Babbage was a great inventor.
Ⓓ Babbage had a good idea.

10. Which of these statements from the essay cannot be proved?

Ⓐ Today, lots of people write computer programs.
Ⓑ They named the programming language Ada after her.
Ⓒ The first machine was the difference engine.
Ⓓ History is often unfair.

11. Which of these statements about Lovelace is an opinion?

Ⓐ She also wrote about uses for the computer.
Ⓑ She was a countess.
Ⓒ She was great at math.
Ⓓ She wrote the first program.

12. Which statement about Babbage's second machine can be proved?

Ⓐ It was the most important idea of the time.
Ⓑ Everyone says he invented the computer.
Ⓒ The machine was the analytical engine.
Ⓓ The idea showed how clever Babbage was.

▶ A test question about distinguishing between fact and opinion may ask you to tell if a statement is a fact or an opinion.

▶ To recognize a fact, read each answer choice, and ask yourself, "Can this statement be proved?" If it can, then it is a fact.

▶ To recognize an opinion, read each answer choice, and ask yourself, "Does this statement tell what someone thinks or feels?" If it does, then it is an opinion. Look in the answer choices for clue words that signal an opinion.

Here is a news article about exploring Mars. Read the article. Then do Numbers 13 and 14.

The most interesting space study began in January 2002. That's when the Odyssey began taking pictures of Mars. Odyssey will orbit Mars for several years. It will send the best information about Mars to scientists. Scientists have never been more excited. They all want to know if Mars has water.

In 1887, an Italian looked through his telescope. He believed he saw lines on Mars. He called them *canali*. In Italian, *canali* means channels. But English speakers thought he meant canals. Canals are waterways built by people. So, people thought that some form of life must have built them. Soon everyone believed there was life on Mars! Scientists later decided there was no water and no life on Mars.

Other spacecrafts have orbited Mars. They seemed to prove there was no water. But more pictures have been taken in recent years. The pictures showed places where water might be found.

Odyssey will show if there is water on Mars. The most puzzling question about the red planet might soon be answered.

Distinguishing Between Fact and Opinion

13. Which of these is an opinion from the article?

   Ⓐ Odyssey will orbit Mars for several years.
   Ⓑ Scientists have never been more excited.
   Ⓒ Canals are waterways built by people.
   Ⓓ He called them *canali*.

Distinguishing Between Fact and Opinion

14. Which of these is a fact from the article?

   Ⓐ The most interesting space study began in January 2002.
   Ⓑ More pictures have been taken in recent years.
   Ⓒ Soon everyone believed there was life on Mars!
   Ⓓ It will send the best information about Mars to scientists.

Here is a student's report on jaguars. Read the report.
Then do Numbers 15 and 16.

Of all the large cats, I think the jaguar is the most handsome. This wild cat lives in the steamy rain forests of South America. It is also found in lands with marshes and low brush in North America and South America. You can find a few jaguars in zoos. A zoo is the least dangerous place for you to see one.

The jaguar has a beautiful coat. The main color is a soft gray, tan, yellow, or red. Dotted on this color is a design of small black circles. These circles may be filled with a color darker than the main color. The tip of the tail can have black and white stripes. White fur often surrounds the jaguar's face.

The jaguar is the largest cat of North America and South America. A jaguar can grow to be 6 feet long. It can weigh 400 pounds. Jaguars eat mostly mammals. They also eat reptiles and fish. Rare accounts of jaguars attacking humans have been recorded. Such a jaguar would be the worst kind of jaguar to meet in the wild.

Distinguishing Between Fact and Opinion

15. Which of these is an opinion from the report?

   Ⓐ The jaguar is the largest cat of North America and South America.

   Ⓑ Jaguars eat mostly mammals.

   Ⓒ Rare accounts of jaguars attacking humans have been recorded.

   Ⓓ Such a jaguar would be the worst kind of jaguar to meet in the wild.

Distinguishing Between Fact and Opinion

16. Which of these is a fact from the report?

   Ⓐ Of all the large cats, I think the jaguar is the most handsome.

   Ⓑ A zoo is the least dangerous place for you to see one.

   Ⓒ The jaguar has a beautiful coat.

   Ⓓ A jaguar can grow to be 6 feet long.

PART ONE: Read a Biography

Here is a short biography about a pilot. Read the biography.
Then do Numbers 1 through 6.

Bessie Coleman, Into the Air

Bessie Coleman dreamed of making something of herself. She was born in Texas in 1892. As a young girl, she wanted to learn math. When she did not have to work in the fields, Bessie walked four miles to a tiny school.

Bessie also liked to read. A library wagon came down her road twice a year. Bessie's mother rented books for Bessie to read. Bessie often chose books about African Americans.

Soon Bessie craved a better education. The school she attended wasn't very good. So she ironed shirts to earn money. The work was boring. But she earned enough to go to a school in Oklahoma for one term.

One of Bessie's brothers lived in Chicago. So Bessie went there in 1915 to find a job. In 1919, she heard about French pilots who were women. So Bessie decided she would become an aviatrix, too.

Bessie read articles in the *Chicago Defender* about these pilots. She discussed her dream with the owner of the newspaper. He told her to learn French and then travel to France. She worked, saved, and studied. Finally, in 1920, Bessie sailed to France.

Each day, Bessie walked nine miles to a flying school and then back to her room. She knew that being a pilot could be dangerous, but that did not stop her. She learned how to fly.

In 1921, Bessie headed home with her pilot's license. She was the happiest person in the world! Her name was in all the newspapers. She was the first female African-American pilot.

Bessie flew planes in America and then returned to Europe for awhile. There, she learned daring stunts. At home, big crowds came to her shows. Bessie's airshows were more exciting than anyone else's. Most important, she told her fans that everyone can fly high.

Finding Word Meaning in Context

1. In paragraph three, the word *craved* means

Ⓐ "disliked."
Ⓑ "refused."
Ⓒ "desired."
Ⓓ "gave herself."

Finding Word Meaning in Context

2. You can tell that the word *aviatrix* in paragraph four means

Ⓐ "a student of math."
Ⓑ "a female pilot."
Ⓒ "a person living in Chicago."
Ⓓ "a famous writer."

Drawing Conclusions and Making Inferences

3. From the biography, you can tell that Bessie Coleman was

Ⓐ lazy and hard to please.
Ⓑ determined and brave.
Ⓒ shy and kind.
Ⓓ weak and sickly.

Drawing Conclusions and Making Inferences

4. In paragraph five, details help you conclude that the *Chicago Defender* is a

Ⓐ long book.
Ⓑ famous lawyer.
Ⓒ newspaper.
Ⓓ police officer.

Distinguishing Between Fact and Opinion

5. Which of these is a fact?

Ⓐ A library wagon came down her road twice a year.
Ⓑ The school she attended wasn't very good.
Ⓒ The work was boring.
Ⓓ Bessie's airshows were more exciting than anyone else's.

Distinguishing Between Fact and Opinion

6. Which of these is an opinion?

Ⓐ Bessie went to Chicago in 1915 to find a job.
Ⓑ Bessie flew planes in America and then returned to Europe.
Ⓒ Bessie often chose books about African Americans.
Ⓓ She was the happiest person in the world!

Here is an entry from Lisa's journal. Read the journal entry. Then do Numbers 7 through 12.

Tuesday, March 1

Today was the worst day. It started when my mother woke me up 15 minutes late, and I had to hurry to get dressed. I grabbed an apple and caught the bus just in time. My hair was a mess, but that wasn't the worst part. I had buttoned my sweater wrong, and I had on two different socks. I looked foolish.

At school, I rushed to the girl's room, fixed my sweater, and took off my socks, which made me late to homeroom. Mr. Thompson sent me to the office. When I got there, six other students were waiting to see Ms. Rider. By the time I got to my first class, I was late again. The class was taking the hardest test we've ever had. I didn't finish, and Miss West wouldn't give me extra time.

At lunch, the spaghetti slid off my plate. The janitor glared at me and said I could use his pail and sponge to clean up my mess. The water in the pail was brown, but I had to do the horrible job.

I asked for another lunch, but I didn't have enough money. The clerk wouldn't let me use credit because she said that I already owed for two lunches. I didn't owe any money, but what could I do? I bought a juice.

At 2:10, I started talking to Jane and, before I knew it, my bus had left. I was supposed to come right home from school to go to the dentist. My mother was annoyed. She had to pick me up at school and take me to the dentist, so we were late. When I told my mother about my day, she wasn't upset anymore. She gave me a hug and promised to get me my own alarm clock.

Finding Word Meaning in Context

7. In paragraph three, which phrase gives a clue to the meaning of the word *janitor*?

   Ⓐ spaghetti slid off my plate.
   Ⓑ his pail and sponge to clean up
   Ⓒ water in the pail was brown
   Ⓓ glared at me

Finding Word Meaning in Context

8. In paragraph four, the best meaning of the word *credit* is

   Ⓐ "the normal price."
   Ⓑ "a loan of money."
   Ⓒ "a free lunch."
   Ⓓ "the exact change."

Drawing Conclusions and Making Inferences

9. From the journal entry, you can tell that Lisa

   Ⓐ doesn't like school.
   Ⓑ does poorly in her subjects.
   Ⓒ cares about the way she looks.
   Ⓓ has only one friend, Jane.

Drawing Conclusions and Making Inferences

10. Which detail from the journal entry helped you answer question 9?

    Ⓐ At 2:10, I started talking to Jane and, before I knew it, my bus had left.
    Ⓑ At school, I rushed to the girl's room, fixed my sweater, and took off my socks, which made me late to homeroom.
    Ⓒ The water in the pail was brown, but I had to do the horrible job.
    Ⓓ I didn't finish, and Miss West wouldn't give me extra time.

Distinguishing Between Fact and Opinion

11. Which of these statements is an opinion?

    Ⓐ Mr. Thompson sent me to the office.
    Ⓑ I bought a juice.
    Ⓒ By the time I got to my first class, I was late again.
    Ⓓ The class was taking the hardest test we've ever had.

Distinguishing Between Fact and Opinion

12. Which of these statements is a fact?

    Ⓐ Today was the worst day.
    Ⓑ My hair was a mess, but that wasn't the worst part.
    Ⓒ I had buttoned my sweater wrong, and I had on two different socks.
    Ⓓ I looked foolish.

10 Identifying Author's Purpose

PART ONE: Learn About Identifying Author's Purpose

Read this paragraph that is adapted from a story by Edgar Allan Poe. As you read, think about why the author probably wrote the paragraph.

The room was very large and lofty, with long, narrow windows. They were pointed at the top and set at a vast distance from the black oak floor. They could not even be reached from inside the room. Weak gleams of reddish light made their way through the panes. The light lit up objects in the center of the room, but did not reach into the corners or to the ceiling. Dark drapes hung sadly on the walls. The furniture was antique and tattered.

The author probably wrote the paragraph to help readers picture the room. The author's purpose is to describe a scene.

All authors write for a reason. The reason an author writes something is called author's purpose. When you figure out why a reading passage was written, you are **identifying author's purpose**. Authors write for one of four main reasons—to describe, to entertain, to explain, or to persuade.

- If a reading passage contains many details about a person, place, or thing, the author's purpose is to **describe**.

- If a reading passage is enjoyable to read, tells a personal story, or uses a story to teach a lesson, the author's purpose is to **entertain**.

- If a reading passage provides facts about a particular subject or tells readers how to do something, the author's purpose is to **explain**.

- If a reading passage tries to get readers to do something, buy something, or believe something, the author's purpose is to **persuade**.

Read this poem about a person and his cat. As you read, try to figure out the author's purpose for writing the poem. Then answer the questions.

The Challenge of Shadowing My Cat

Into the alley I followed my cat,
I walked where she walked, I sat where she sat.
Her eyes darted up as she saw birds fly by;
She ran a few steps and so did I.
But when she meowed while twitching her tail,
And leaped for a mouse, I knew I would fail.
I left the alley and said, "That is that!
I cannot be my cat's copycat."

1. The author wrote the poem mainly to

- Ⓐ explain what cats do in alleys at night.
- Ⓑ try to get readers to adopt a cat for a pet.
- Ⓒ describe a beautiful cat and the person who owns the cat.
- Ⓓ entertain readers with a funny poem.

2. You know your answer to question 1 is correct because the poem mainly

- Ⓐ describes a person, place, or thing.
- Ⓑ contains lots of information about something.
- Ⓒ tries to convince readers of something.
- Ⓓ tells something personal and amusing.

Work with a partner. Talk about your answers to questions 1 and 2. Tell why you chose the answers you did.

PART TWO: Check Your Understanding

Remember: Authors write to describe, to entertain, to explain, or to persuade.

▶ As you read, ask yourself, "Does the reading passage contain many details that describe a person, a place, or a thing?" If so, the author's purpose is to describe.

▶ As you read, ask yourself, "Does the reading passage tell an enjoyable or a personal story? Does the author use a story to teach a lesson?" If so, the author's purpose is to entertain.

▶ As you read, ask yourself, "Does the reading passage provide facts about a particular subject? Does the passage tell me how to do something?" If so, the author's purpose is to explain.

▶ As you read, ask yourself, "Does the reading passage try to convince me to do something, buy something, or believe something?" If so, the author's purpose is to persuade.

Read this ad from a school newspaper. As you read, ask yourself, "Why did the author probably write this ad?" Then answer the questions.

Swing Over to Try Out!

Do you like to act on stage? Dance? Sing? Perform silly stunts?

This spring, the Drama Club will present *The Swing* based on the novel by Albert Green. The play is really a fun project!

The Swing has many parts available. If you like to be seen, there's a part for you. If not, you can hide behind a screen and just sing. If you like working with small groups—or large groups—there's a part for you. If you like to dress up, some parts require fantastic costumes.

Please come to tryouts on January 22. We will find the right part for you!

3. The author wrote the ad mainly to
  Ⓐ persuade students to try out for a play.
  Ⓑ explain how a book can be rewritten as a play.
  Ⓒ describe some characters in *The Swing*.
  Ⓓ entertain readers with a story about putting on a play.

4. You know your answer to question 3 is correct because the ad mainly
  Ⓐ contains many details that describe something.
  Ⓑ provides facts or tells readers how to do something.
  Ⓒ tries to convince readers to do something.
  Ⓓ tells an enjoyable story.

Look at the answer choices for each question.
Read why each answer choice is correct or not correct.

3. The author wrote the ad mainly to

● persuade students to try out for a play.

This answer is correct because the ad contains lots of convincing reasons that students should try out for the play.

Ⓑ explain how a book can be rewritten as a play.

This answer is not correct because the ad does not contain facts or other information about rewriting a book as a play. The ad only mentions that the play is based on a book.

Ⓒ describe some characters in The Swing.

This answer is not correct because the ad does not contain any details about the characters in the play.

Ⓓ entertain readers with a story about putting on a play.

This answer is not correct because the ad does not tell an interesting story or try to make readers laugh. Also, the author does not tell a story to teach a lesson.

4. You know your answer to question 3 is correct because the ad mainly

Ⓐ contains many details that describe something.

This answer is not correct because the ad does not mainly contain details that describe a particular person, place, or thing. There are a few details, but they all support the purpose of persuading.

Ⓑ provides facts or tells readers how to do something.

This answer is not correct because the ad does not mainly provide facts or tell readers how to do something. The facts that are included explain what the writer wants students to try out for and when.

● tries to convince readers to do something.

This answer is correct because the ad contains many opinions about the play and the parts available. Details suggest why students should try out for the play. The ad tries to convince students that they will get a good part and have fun.

Ⓓ tells an enjoyable story.

This answer is not correct because the ad does not tell an enjoyable story or try to make readers laugh, nor does the author use a story to teach a lesson. Also, the ad does not contain a series of events leading to an ending.

PART THREE: Learn More About Identifying Author's Purpose

Different reading passages are written for different purposes. Knowing the kind of passage you are reading often helps you identify the author's purpose.

▶ Articles are usually written to describe or explain. Some articles describe a person, place, or thing. Other articles explain something, such as how a CD works.

▶ Directions are written to explain. Directions tell you how to do something.

▶ Personal stories, folktales, poems, and other stories are written to entertain. They may also be written to teach a lesson.

▶ Ads, articles, and letters in which an opinion is stated are written to persuade. They try to get people to believe something, do something, or buy something.

Read each passage. Then answer the questions.

I.

Are you looking for a thrilling ride? Then come to France and ride the fastest passenger trains in the world. On the straight and level track, you will rush along at up to 186 miles per hour! Don't miss the trip from Paris to Lyon! It's the best!

II.

What did the track say to the train?
Don't make a move without me.

How do you train a seal?
Keep it on track.

III.

When I stepped onto the platform to board the train to the city, I saw the old man. He had on a dark suit, rather worn, and a dull red bow tie that was tied unevenly. Over his arm hung a brown coat. He looked tired and unhappy.

IV.

Most trains run on a track with two rails. The track directs the train, so that no one has to steer. The power for some trains comes from the burning of diesel fuel. Some trains run on electricity from overhead wires or a third rail.

5. The author's main purpose in passage I is to
   - Ⓐ describe.
   - Ⓑ explain.
   - Ⓒ entertain.
   - Ⓓ persuade.

6. The author's main purpose in passage II is to
   - Ⓐ describe.
   - Ⓑ explain.
   - Ⓒ entertain.
   - Ⓓ persuade.

7. The author's main purpose in passage III is to
   - Ⓐ describe.
   - Ⓑ explain.
   - Ⓒ entertain.
   - Ⓓ persuade.

8. The author's main purpose in passage IV is to
   - Ⓐ describe.
   - Ⓑ explain.
   - Ⓒ entertain.
   - Ⓓ persuade.

Dear Mark,

    I can give you four great reasons for coming to Camp Greymount. First, the canoeing on Silver Lake is exciting. Second, the lodge has tasty food. Third, camping out on the mountain is terrific. Fourth, I'm here, and we'd have twice as much fun together. Ask your parents to bring you.

    A funny thing happened on my last camp-out. I had just settled into my tent when I heard a loud whirring noise. I peeked out the window in the tent's roof. I expected to see a huge animal, but the sound was a moth beating against the window netting.

    The area around Camp Greymount is beautiful. The lodge rests in a green valley at the base of the mountain. I can see Silver Lake from my window. In the morning, mist rises up from the lake like a scene from a mystery story. Tall pine trees stand like guards around the beach.

    It's easy to get to Camp Greymount. Take route 46 to exit 15A. Off the exit ramp, take a sharp right and travel nine miles to Harris. At the first traffic light, turn left on Misty Road and you'll see the signs to Camp Greymount.

Hope to see you soon,
Juan

9. The author wrote paragraph one mainly to

  Ⓐ explain who runs the camp.
  Ⓑ persuade Mark to come to Camp Greymount.
  Ⓒ describe the lodge.
  Ⓓ entertain Mark with a joke about camp.

10. The author wrote paragraph two mainly to

  Ⓐ tell how moths fly.
  Ⓑ convince Mark to sleep outside.
  Ⓒ describe what tents look like.
  Ⓓ entertain Mark with a personal story.

11. What is the author's purpose in paragraph three?

  Ⓐ to get Mark to bring a camera
  Ⓑ to amuse Mark with a mystery story about the lake
  Ⓒ to describe the landscape
  Ⓓ to explain why mist rises up from the lake

12. The author's purpose in paragraph four is to

  Ⓐ explain how to get to the camp.
  Ⓑ persuade Mark to get his parents to bring him to camp.
  Ⓒ describe the sights near the camp.
  Ⓓ relate enjoyable information.

▐▌ A test question about identifying the author's purpose may ask you why an author probably wrote a particular reading passage. This kind of question is asking about the purpose of the entire reading passage.

▐▌ A test question about identifying the author's purpose may ask you why a particular paragraph was written. This kind of question is asking about only one part of the reading passage.

Here is an article about a Native-American art form. Read the article. Then do Numbers 13 and 14.

The Ojibway Dreamcatcher

The dreamcatcher is an art form that has been made by the Ojibway for centuries. The dreamcatcher has a round frame, often made of wood. Inside the frame, thin threads made of hide form the shape of a web with a small hole in the middle.

To the Ojibway, the dreamcatcher is more than a piece of art. It is a symbol of the link between real life and dream life. It also protects children. The web catches the bad dreams that might come to a sleeping child. The small hole lets the good dreams come through.

An Ojibway myth tells that Spider Woman gave the dreamcatcher to the Ojibway people. Long ago, Spider Woman was weaving her web near Grandmother's bed. Everyday, Grandmother admired the beauty of the web. One day, her grandson noticed Spider Woman. The boy went to kill her with his moccasin. Grandmother saved Spider Woman, who offered her a gift. The gift was the knowledge of how to make a web, a dreamcatcher, to protect the Ojibway people from bad dreams.

Identifying Author's Purpose

13. What is the author's purpose in the last paragraph?
  Ⓐ to tell how a dreamcatcher is made
  Ⓑ to entertain readers with a myth about the dreamcatcher
  Ⓒ to make readers want to buy a dreamcatcher
  Ⓓ to describe the beauty of a dreamcatcher

Identifying Author's Purpose

14. The author wrote the article mainly to
  Ⓐ describe the materials used to make Ojibway dreamcatchers.
  Ⓑ amuse readers with an entertaining story.
  Ⓒ convince readers to make their own dreamcatchers.
  Ⓓ explain what a dreamcatcher is and what it means to the Ojibway people.

Here is a retelling of a fable by Aesop. Read the fable.
Then do Numbers 15 and 16.

Stubborn as a Goat

Two goats lived near a river. One lived on the north side, and the other on the south side. Daily, they wandered over the rocky land looking for tasty bushes to eat.

The goat on the north side had a warm gray coat. Each fuzzy ear stood straight up and ended in a sharp point. He had two small horns and a short tail that waved side to side when he got angry.

One day, he was climbing rocks near the river. The same day, the other goat was climbing rocks across the river. This goat had long white fur, floppy ears, two curved horns, and a soft tail. His tail waved up and down when he was angry.

Both goats found a log that had fallen across the river. The gray goat strolled boldly onto the log as the white goat jumped onto it from the other side. Both walked to the middle, but the log was too narrow to let either goat pass.

"Go back so I can pass," ordered the gray goat.

"No, you go back," demanded the white goat.

They stayed there, hour after hour, each one too stubborn to move. They became more and more angry until their tails wagged so strongly that the log broke loose and fell into the water. Both goats were carried away by the river's flow.

Identifying Author's Purpose

15. The author wrote paragraph two mainly to

    Ⓐ explain where goats live.
    Ⓑ describe the gray goat.
    Ⓒ convince readers that the gray goat is stubborn.
    Ⓓ entertain readers with humorous details about the odd things goats do.

Identifying Author's Purpose

16. The fable was written mainly to

    Ⓐ describe a rocky river landscape.
    Ⓑ explain how two goats tried to cross a river.
    Ⓒ amuse readers with a story that teaches a lesson about being stubborn.
    Ⓓ persuade readers to take a goat for a pet.

11 Interpreting Figurative Language

PART ONE: Learn About Interpreting Figurative Language

Read this sentence. As you read, think about the two things being compared.

The dog sat like a stone statue on the steps.

The two things being compared are a dog and a statue.
The writer used a **simile** to help readers picture how still the dog was sitting.
A simile uses the word *like* or *as* to compare two things.

Read this sentence. As you read, think about the two things being compared.

The falling snow was flour tossed from the clouds.

The two things being compared are falling snow and flour.
The writer used a **metaphor** to help readers picture the sight of the falling snow.
A metaphor compares two things but does not use the word *like* or *as*.
A metaphor says that one thing is another thing.

Now read this sentence. As you read, think about the meaning of
the underlined words.

Jenna <u>let the cat out of the bag</u> when she told Pedro about his surprise party.

The underlined words mean "told a secret." The underlined words are an **idiom**.
An idiom is a phrase in which words have a meaning different from their usual meaning.

Similes, metaphors, and idioms are types of figurative language.
Authors use figurative language to help readers create pictures in their mind.
When you understand the meaning of a simile, a metaphor, or an idiom,
you are **interpreting figurative language**.

▶ Look for things that are compared in a reading passage.
   Try to find examples of similes or metaphors.

▶ Look for phrases whose words have a meaning different from their usual
   meaning. Try to find examples of idioms.

▶ Figurative language usually brings a picture to a reader's mind. Use that
   picture to help you understand the meaning of the figurative language.

Read this poem. As you read, ask yourself, "What pictures come to mind?"
Then answer the questions.

Autumn Storm

The wind rustled the trees like a woman shaking a rug.
The branches creaked and clapped together.
The leaves were dancers, tumbling toward the ground,
Then running and leaping over the heather.

Gray birds held onto a tree limb in the wind that
Stirred their feathers and rumpled their form.
Heads down, they looked like a crowd of people
Waiting for a bus in the growing storm.

The clouds, playing follow-the-leader with the wind,
Brought frozen rain like grains of falling rice.
The wind blew colder and colder. The land
Was a silvery, shadowy glow of autumn ice.

1. In the poem, the birds are compared to

Ⓐ a limb of a tree.

Ⓑ clouds.

Ⓒ a crowd of people.

Ⓓ dancers.

2. In the first stanza, what is the wind compared to?

Ⓐ branches creaking and clapping

Ⓑ dancers running

Ⓒ a woman shaking a rug

Ⓓ trees

Work with a partner. Talk about your answers to questions 1 and 2.
Tell why you chose the answers you did.

PART TWO: Check Your Understanding

Remember: Similes, metaphors, and idioms are types of figurative language. Authors use figurative language to help readers create clear pictures in their mind.

▶ Look for things that are compared in a reading passage. See if the word *like* or *as* is used, or if a sentence says that one thing is another thing.

▶ Look for phrases in which words have a meaning different from their usual meaning.

▶ Think about any pictures that come to mind as you read. Use those pictures to help you understand what is being described.

Read this article about R. Carlos Nakai, a Native-American flute player. As you read, look for things that are compared. Also look for words that have a meaning different from their usual meaning. Then answer the questions.

The Waves of the Flute

For the people of the Americas, the custom of playing the flute flows back in history. Flute playing goes back more than 2,500 years. We know this from songs passed down over the ages. We also know this from ancient pictures of flute players carved in stone. R. Carlos Nakai carries on this ancient tradition today.

Nakai's songs are like prayers floating on the wind. With haunting melodies, the songs tell of his people's beliefs. His music also reveals his feelings about nature. He plays songs of soaring hawks and of desert winds. The music is a picture of the landscape.

You are not likely to hear Nakai on the radio. But he has made many CDs that you might enjoy. So turn over a new leaf and try a new type of old music, Nakai's Native-American flute playing. You might find yourself in a land of wonder.

---

3. In paragraph two, Nakai's songs are compared to

Ⓐ hawks.

Ⓑ prayers.

Ⓒ music.

Ⓓ wind.

4. In the last paragraph, the phrase *turn over a new leaf* means

Ⓐ "rake the yard."

Ⓑ "open a book."

Ⓒ "try something different."

Ⓓ "look for something that is missing."

Look at the answer choices for each question.
Read why each answer choice is correct or not correct.

3. In paragraph two, Nakai's songs are compared to

Ⓐ hawks.

This answer is not correct because soaring hawks are one thing the songs tell about, not something the songs are compared to.

● prayers.

This answer is correct because the article states "Nakai's songs are like prayers floating on the wind." The word like *is a signal of the comparison.*

Ⓒ music.

This answer is not correct because there is no comparison between music and the songs. The songs are music, but this is not a comparison.

Ⓓ wind.

This answer is not correct because the songs are not compared to the wind. The article states that the desert winds are one of the subjects of the songs.

4. In the last paragraph, the phrase *turn over a new leaf* means

Ⓐ "rake the yard."

This answer is not correct because the last paragraph is about listening to music. There are no details in this paragraph, or in the article, that tell about raking.

Ⓑ "open a book."

This answer is not correct because there are no details in the last paragraph that suggest this meaning or describe anything about a book.

● "try something different."

This answer is correct because the details in the last paragraph hint at this meaning. Right after the phrase turn over a new leaf, *the writer states, ". . . try a new type of old music . . . ."*

Ⓓ "look for something that is missing."

This answer is not correct because there are no details in the last paragraph that suggest this meaning. Someone who wants to turn over a new leaf is not looking for something that is lost. Rather, the person is looking to try something new.

PART THREE: Learn More About Interpreting Figurative Language

▶ Think about the things being compared in a simile or a metaphor. Ask yourself, "What do the two things have in common?" This will help you create pictures in your mind.

▶ Look at the sentences near an idiom. You might find context clues to help you figure out its meaning.

Read this myth about how the monkey got its long tail. Then answer the questions.

Longing for Safety

Long ago, Monkey had a short tail. One day, Monkey passed a cottage. His curiosity called him inside. Then a noise as loud as a firecracker made him run for the door. As he slipped out, the door slammed shut. Monkey's tail got caught.

Monkey couldn't reach the door handle, so he leaned against the door thinking about what to do. Just then, Mosquito buzzed toward Monkey, but Monkey didn't want to be bitten. Monkey wriggled and pulled like a dog on a leash, but he could not get free. Mosquito just flew past to dance on the wind.

Soon Snake slid toward Monkey. Monkey didn't want to be lunch for Snake, so Monkey pulled and pulled on his tail, but he was still stuck. Snake just wiggled past Monkey to dip in the stream.

Then Tiger, huge and hungry, stalked toward the cottage door. Now Monkey was really in a bind! He tugged and pulled frantically not caring if his tail broke. Just in time, his tail slipped free, and Monkey raced off. His tail had stretched to ten times its length. It dangled like a rope behind him as he ran.

5. The noise Monkey hears in the cottage is compared to

Ⓐ a door slamming.
Ⓑ a firecracker.
Ⓒ a box dropping.
Ⓓ a sharp bang.

6. Paragraph two says that Monkey *pulled like a dog on a leash*. This means that Monkey

Ⓐ pulled gently.
Ⓑ tugged strongly and impatiently.
Ⓒ barked as he pulled.
Ⓓ tugged carefully and calmly.

7. In the last paragraph, the phrase *in a bind* means

Ⓐ "had his tail caught."
Ⓑ "was tugging as hard as he could."
Ⓒ "had a big problem."
Ⓓ "was leaning too hard against the door."

8. In the last paragraph, Monkey's tail is compared to a rope because the tail is

Ⓐ caught in a door.
Ⓑ wrapped around his body.
Ⓒ tied up.
Ⓓ long and hanging loosely.

Read this modern tall tale about an astronaut. Then answer the questions.

Luna in the Sky

Luna Marias seemed like an ordinary baby. When she was two days old, she jumped up and raced around the house like a bullet train. Her scream was the whistle. At three days old, Luna kept leaping into the air like a huge rabbit, all day long.

"What's gotten into that girl's head?" her dad asked.

"Goodness, I can't imagine," her mom answered.

But on her fourth day, Luna answered her dad's question, "I want to travel in space."

"Don't bite off more than you can chew, little one," her dad warned. But when he realized she was as tall as he was, he said, "Okay."

At five days old, Luna headed for space camp. The next day, she was almost too big for the rockets. She begged her teachers to send her into space, so they stuffed her into the largest rocket.

"Blast off," she yelled as loud as a clap of thunder. At lightning speed, the rocket raced 239,000 miles before it burst. "I'll stop here and sleep for a few million years," she yelled. Then she curled up into a ball. She's still there, up in the sky. Luna Marias is our moon!

9. What did Luna's dad mean when he asked, *What's gotten into that girl's head?*

   Ⓐ "What kind of hat is Luna wearing?"
   Ⓑ "Why isn't Luna answering the question?"
   Ⓒ "What is Luna thinking?"
   Ⓓ "How does Luna wear her hair?"

10. Which of these is a metaphor?

   Ⓐ The next day, she was almost too big for the rockets.
   Ⓑ At five days old, Luna headed for space camp.
   Ⓒ Her scream was the whistle.
   Ⓓ She's still there, up in the sky.

11. In paragraph five, *bite off more than you can chew* means

   Ⓐ "choke on a piece of food."
   Ⓑ "attempt to do more than you can."
   Ⓒ "eat greedily."
   Ⓓ "do something because others are doing it."

12. In the last paragraph, when Luna yelled, her voice is compared to

   Ⓐ a clap of thunder.
   Ⓑ lightning.
   Ⓒ a rocket.
   Ⓓ a ball.

▶ A test question about interpreting figurative language may ask you about the meaning of a simile, a metaphor, or an idiom.

▶ A test question about interpreting figurative language may ask you to identify a particular type of figurative language, such as a simile, a metaphor, or an idiom.

Here is a newspaper ad. Read the ad. Then do Numbers 13 and 14.

Do you want to make your home or office livelier? Who wouldn't? But maybe you can't get your plans off the ground.

At Plants for All, we can help you get started. We have all the plants needed to trim your house. We have plants to make your workplace really green. You may even be successful enough to open a new branch office.

Come to 15 Laurel Lane to see our selection of choice plants. Our tree shop is like a forest. Our bush and shrub area is packed with plants. Our greenhouse flowers are a rainbow of colors.

You'll appreciate our sales clerks. They are well trained and honest. They don't beat around the bush. They tell you what will work for you. They'll go out on a limb and take back any plant you aren't totally happy with.

So don't be a stick-in-the-mud. Come visit us as soon as possible. Your friends will be green with envy and you'll be tickled pink!

Interpreting Figurative Language

13. In paragraph four, the phrase *go out on a limb* means
   Ⓐ "crawl on a branch to trim it."
   Ⓑ "walk over someone's arm."
   Ⓒ "create a new type of plant."
   Ⓓ "take a risk."

Interpreting Figurative Language

14. Which sentence includes a simile?
   Ⓐ You'll appreciate our sales clerks.
   Ⓑ Our tree shop is like a forest.
   Ⓒ Come visit us as soon as possible.
   Ⓓ Our greenhouse flowers are a rainbow of colors.

Here is a letter written by a girl named Olivia. Read the letter. Then do Numbers 15 and 16.

Dear Aunt Agatha,

I love brainteasers more than anyone, and I'm usually clever at solving them. But your last letter is making my head spin. You gave me a riddle to solve about a house that is sometimes as beautiful as a peacock. At other times it is frightening, like a sudden howl in the night. You said that if the house were a snake, it would bite me. So I guess the house must be near where I live.

I asked my parents to help me solve your riddle, but they are as perplexed as I am. Could you give me another clue, or let me know if I'm on the right track?

I've been like a squirrel searching for a nut. I checked all the old homes around here. Mr. Jones's home is a huge junk heap that no one can go near. The farmhouse on Silver Street is as pretty as a picture, but not beautiful or scary. Mrs. Stein's big house is as plain as a blank page. I know you wouldn't call that beautiful.

You can see that I am at a loss. Please save me from running around in circles, and help me solve this riddle.

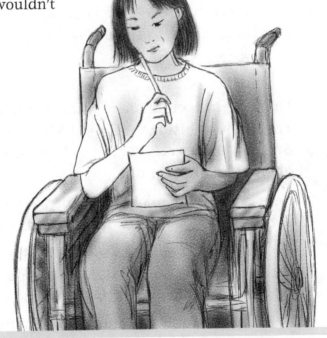

Your niece,
Olivia, the Detective

Interpreting Figurative Language

15. In the first paragraph, the phrase *making my head spin* means that Olivia is

Ⓐ confused.
Ⓑ clever.
Ⓒ frightened.
Ⓓ amused.

Interpreting Figurative Language

16. In paragraph three, Olivia compares herself to a

Ⓐ peacock.
Ⓑ picture.
Ⓒ squirrel.
Ⓓ blank page.

Summarizing

PART ONE: Learn About Summarizing

Read this article about dogs. The most important ideas in the article are underlined. These are the ideas that you might use to tell someone who asks what the article is about.

Woofing Workers

Throughout history, different kinds of dogs have helped people. Today, the American Kennel Club lists over 140 breeds of dogs. Some of these breeds are trained to guide a person without sight or work with a deaf owner. Other breeds are trained to help the police. Because they work, some modern dogs are like the dogs first tamed about 10,000 years ago. Dogs were first trained as watchdogs. They would bark if a stranger came near. Later, some dogs were taught to help with hunting. Then people taught other types of dogs to guard sheep and cattle.

The most important ideas in the article are
**Throughout history, different kinds of dogs have helped people.
Because they work, some modern dogs are like the dogs first tamed
about 10,000 years ago.**

Here is what you might tell someone who asks what the article is about:
For about 10,000 years, some breeds of dogs have worked to help people.

The statement above is a summary. A summary is a short statement that tells the main points or important ideas of a reading passage. When you restate the important ideas in a short statement, you are **summarizing**.

▶ A summary is not stated in a reading passage. To create a summary, you must think about and restate the most important ideas.

▶ A good summary of fiction tells about the main character's problem and its solution.

▶ A good summary of nonfiction tells about the main idea of the reading selection, as well as the main idea of each paragraph.

Read this story about a boy in the city. As you read, think about the main character's problem and its solution. Then answer the questions.

"Oh no!" Jarod exclaimed at the bus stop. He checked his watch. The time was 4:35 P.M. He had to be home by 5:00 P.M., which would be easy if he caught the next bus. But Jarod reached into his pocket to find only a hole and no money. Somewhere between Center Street and Lake Avenue, seventy-five cents had hit the pavement and bounced into the unknown. Jarod had no money for the bus.

Jarod sat down at the bus stop and thought about what to do. He could ask someone for the money, but that didn't seem right. He could get on the bus, but the driver would probably put him off. He could walk, but that would take an hour.

Just as the bus approached, Jarod saw something green near the bench. It was a dollar bill. He looked around. There was no one to claim it, so there was no way to return the money to its owner, sort of like the money Jarod had dropped. Jarod picked up the dollar, feeling lucky and thankful. "I'll be more careful next time," he promised himself. "Maybe my seventy-five cents will help some needy person, too," he thought. When the bus pulled up, Jarod got on.

1. What is Jarod's problem in the story?
   Ⓐ He is late for the bus.
   Ⓑ He has lost his money for the bus.
   Ⓒ He has gone to the city without permission.
   Ⓓ The bus he has to take is late.

2. What is the best summary of the story?
   Ⓐ A boy makes a mistake that gets him into trouble.
   Ⓑ A boy misses his bus and returns home late.
   Ⓒ A boy loses his bus money but luckily finds a dollar.
   Ⓓ A boy finds a dollar and keeps it.

Work with a partner. Talk about your answers to questions 1 and 2. Tell why you chose the answers you did.

Remember: **A summary is a short statement that tells the main points or important ideas of a reading passage.**

▶ A good summary of fiction tells about the main character's problem and its solution.

▶ A good summary of nonfiction includes the main ideas of the selection.

Read this article about optical illusions. As you read, ask yourself, "What does a good summary of nonfiction include?" Then answer the questions.

What You See Is Not Always What You Get

What happens when you look down a long, straight street? Trees near you look tall. Ones far down the street look short. The houses near you look large, almost life-sized. The ones far away look small, like dollhouses. You know that the trees and houses down the street are the same size as the ones that are near. The fact that they look smaller is a trick of sight. This is called an optical illusion.

The word *optical* refers to sight. *Illusion* means "something that is not real." The words together mean that you are tricked by the way something looks.

If you look at the picture to the right, you may first see a young girl, facing away. If you look longer, you may see an old woman with a large nose.

3. What is the main idea of the article?
   Ⓐ Sometimes, what the eye sees is not what is real.
   Ⓑ Houses look smaller the farther away they are.
   Ⓒ An optical illusion can be a picture.
   Ⓓ The word *optical* refers to sight.

4. What is a good summary of the article?
   Ⓐ A picture can sometimes be seen in two different ways.
   Ⓑ What you see with your own eyes is never wrong.
   Ⓒ Sometimes, you can be tricked by how you see things.
   Ⓓ Objects look smaller close up and bigger farther away.

Look at the answer choices for each question.
Read why each answer choice is correct or not correct.

3. What is the main idea of the article?

● Sometimes what the eye sees is not what is real.

This answer is correct because it tells what the article is mostly about. The main idea is stated in the title and repeated in the last sentence of the second paragraph. All of the examples that are provided support this main idea.

Ⓑ Houses look smaller the farther away they are.

This answer is not correct because it does not tell what the article is mostly about. This answer tells only one detail about one type of optical illusion.

Ⓒ An optical illusion can be a picture.

This answer is not correct because it does not tell what the article is mostly about. This answer provides one example of a type of optical illusion. This is only one detail in the article.

Ⓓ The word *optical* refers to sight.

This answer is not correct because it does not tell what the article is mostly about. This answer provides the meaning of the word optical, but it does not explain anything about the main idea.

4. What is a good summary of the article?

Ⓐ A picture can sometimes be seen in two different ways.

This answer is not correct because it contains only one idea in the article. A good summary of nonfiction should include all the important ideas in the article.

Ⓑ What you see with your own eyes is never wrong.

This answer is not correct because it is not true according to the article. The article explains that sometimes what you see is a trick of sight.

● Sometimes, you can be tricked by how you see things.

This answer is correct because it includes the most important ideas in the article. The article explains how optical illusions can trick your sight.

Ⓓ Objects look smaller close up and bigger farther away.

This answer is not correct because it is not accurate. The article states that the opposite is an example of one type of optical illusion.

PART THREE: Learn More About Summarizing

▷ A good summary of fiction often tells something about the meaning, or theme, of the passage.

▷ A good summary of nonfiction answers *who, what, when, where, why,* and *how* questions.

Read this article about flamingoes. Then answer the questions.

The flamingo is a bird with long, thin legs that help it wade in the water. Its body is well suited to life in marshes, along lakes, and in shallow seas. Its feet are webbed for swimming and for walking on mud and sand.

The flamingo has a curved bill and a long, slender neck. These features help the bird get food from the water. Hairlike combs on its beak act as filters. They separate tiny plants and animals, called algae, from the water. Most flamingoes eat algae. One type of flamingo, the greater flamingo, reaches deep into the water to snatch up shellfish for food.

The awkward shape and large size of the flamingo does not prevent it from flying. Flamingoes often run to gain speed. Then they lift themselves into the air.

---

5. What is the article mostly about?

Ⓐ birds, such as the flamingo, that wade in water

Ⓑ the size and shape of the flamingo

Ⓒ how the flamingo's features support its way of life

Ⓓ how the flamingo uses water and land to swim and fly

6. What information about the flamingo is provided in the article?

Ⓐ body features that help it swim and find food

Ⓑ the color of its feathers and stiltlike legs

Ⓒ the many differences between two types of flamingoes

Ⓓ countries where it can be found

7. Why are the flamingo's long legs important?

Ⓐ They help the bird walk long distances to find food.

Ⓑ They allow the bird to wade in water.

Ⓒ They help the bird run from animals that would eat it.

Ⓓ They help the bird fly.

8. Which of these best summarizes the article?

Ⓐ Many birds live successfully in water.

Ⓑ The flamingo is a beautiful and colorful bird.

Ⓒ No other bird is like the flamingo.

Ⓓ The flamingo's body helps it live in or near water.

Read this Russian folktale. Then answer the questions.

Ivan the Fool

Before he died, an old man told his three sons, "In respect for me and for our family, guard my grave for three nights after my death." Then the man died.

Two of the sons always spent all their time enjoying themselves. They used their father's money to dress in fine clothes and eat rich food. They lazed about all day and partied and then slept the rest of the night. These two did not respect their father's wishes. Instead, they made the third and youngest son, Ivan, go out alone at night and stand guard. They called Ivan "the fool," and they did not give him any fine clothes to wear. He went about in rags.

For the three nights, Ivan was happy to do what his father had asked. At midnight on the third night, Ivan's father appeared to him. He bowed to his youngest son, and gave him a fine horse to reward him for his faithfulness.

Ivan used the horse to win the hand of the beautiful daughter of the Russian ruler. Ivan lived a happy and rich life, rewarded for his good deeds. His brothers were angry and jealous.

9. What is the main problem in the folktale?

   Ⓐ Two sons do not respect their father's request.
   Ⓑ An old man is dying.
   Ⓒ Three brothers worry about guarding their father's grave.
   Ⓓ A fine horse needs a good home.

10. Why did Ivan guard his father's grave alone?

   Ⓐ He refused to let his brothers help him.
   Ⓑ He did not want to share his father's money.
   Ⓒ His brothers made him go alone.
   Ⓓ Ivan was the only son not afraid of going to the grave.

11. What did the horse help Ivan do?

   Ⓐ protect his father
   Ⓑ punish his brothers
   Ⓒ help the Russian leader
   Ⓓ win a beautiful wife

12. What is a good summary of the folktale?

   Ⓐ A man's jealousy and anger prevent his brothers from helping him.
   Ⓑ Only one of three sons respects his father's wishes and is greatly rewarded.
   Ⓒ A horse appears at the grave of a dead man.
   Ⓓ Three brothers respect their dead father's wishes, but only one is rewarded.

▶ A test question about summarizing may ask you to choose the best summary of a reading passage. When you answer questions about summarizing, first determine if the reading passage is a work of fiction or nonfiction. Then think about what is included in a good summary of fiction and a good summary of nonfiction.

▶ The answer to a test question about summarizing will not be directly stated in the reading passage. You must think about the most important ideas to find the best summary.

Here is an article about cowboys who discovered an amazing place. Read the article. Then do Numbers 13 and 14.

Cliff Houses

One December day, three cowboys rode onto a high mesa in the southwest part of Colorado. The day was cold and snow was falling.

Richard and Al Wetherill, along with Charlie Manson, had ridden onto the mesa chasing stray cattle. Richard glanced across the canyon to the east. He cried out in astonishment. There, halfway up the cliff, a shelf of rock shaded the ruins of a string of stone buildings. A three-story tower stood guard. "It looks just like a palace," whispered the amazed cowboy.

The three men felt drawn to explore the cliff. They climbed down and crossed the canyon. Then they scrambled up to the stone buildings. They found an ancient city with more than 200 rooms! Richard called the place Cliff Palace. The inside of the buildings looked as if people had just left. Clay pots sat in the dusty rooms. A heavy stone ax rested on the floor.

Cliff Palace became known as Mesa Verde, or "green table." Mesa Verde National Park opened in 1906 as one of the first national parks in the United States.

Summarizing

13. The article is mostly about
    Ⓐ the work of cowboys.
    Ⓑ the hard work of finding stray cattle.
    Ⓒ the steps in creating a national park in the early 1900s.
    Ⓓ the accidental discovery of ancients ruins.

Summarizing

14. Which of these best summarizes the article?
    Ⓐ Three cowboys left their cattle on a high mesa to visit a national park.
    Ⓑ Three cowboys chasing cattle came upon and explored ancient ruins, now known as Mesa Verde National Park.
    Ⓒ Mesa Verde became one of the first national parks in 1906.
    Ⓓ Cowboys had to chase stray cattle.

Here is a news story about a boy who plays the guitar. Read the story. Then do Numbers 15 and 16.

Last evening, Atlas Middle School held a talent show featuring many talented students. One boy deserves special mention. His name is Ming Chan, and he performed like a master.

Calmly, Ming walked onto the stage to a small chair. As he sat, he paused to smile at the audience. He positioned his guitar just the way he wanted it. I felt as if I was watching an experienced performer. Then he began to play.

Ming's music stunned the entire crowd. The clear tones of the guitar produced a pleasing melody. Ming played a song he had composed. For a full ten minutes, we were all swept away by the perfect music.

I had the honor of interviewing Ming after the show. He told me his story:

"I have always wanted to play the guitar, but my parents said they could not pay for the instrument or lessons. Sadly, I knew they told the truth. So I read library books and tried to learn about how to play. One day last year, my grandmother visited and she heard me talk about what I had learned from the books. Then she went home. Two weeks later, a huge package arrived for me from my grandmother. It was this guitar! Then she sent money every week for lessons. I have studied hard and practiced daily, but without my grandmother's kindness I would never have played the guitar. I am thankful."

Those of us who heard Ming play are thankful, too!

Summarizing

15. The news story is mostly about

Ⓐ the various acts at a talent show and how the writer felt about each one.

Ⓑ how to play the guitar.

Ⓒ a boy's grandmother.

Ⓓ a boy's skill at playing guitar and the person who made it possible.

Summarizing

16. What is a good summary of the news story?

Ⓐ A boy receives money to buy a beautiful guitar.

Ⓑ A boy is able to develop his talent for playing the guitar due to his grandmother's kindness.

Ⓒ A boy wins a talent contest.

Ⓓ A boy composes a song that his grandmother likes.

PART ONE: Read a Myth

Here is a retelling of a Seneca myth. Read the myth.
Then do Numbers 1 through 6.

Blue Feathers for a Bluebird

Long ago, the Great Spirit made all the animals gray so that they could find the right color for themselves. On a fine spring day, a small gray bird sat on a branch and gazed at the sky. "What a beautiful color!" exclaimed the little bird. "I wish my feathers were as blue as the bright spring sky!"

A voice startled the little bird. "Would you really like feathers the color of the sky?"

"Yes," answered the bird hopefully.

"What would you do to be such a blue?" the voice asked.

"I'd sing and give thanks," the bird answered.

"I am the Great Spirit. For the next four mornings, dip into the lake, fly back here, and sing."

So the next four mornings, the bird dipped into the lake even though the water was as gray as a rain cloud. Then the bird flew to the branch and sang. But not a flash of blue showed in the bird's feathers.

"Are you sure you want to be blue?" a deep voice asked on the fourth morning.

"Yes! The Great Spirit promised," the bird answered, "and he does not break his word."

"I am the Great Spirit. Dip again but touch nothing but water. Then fly to the sky and sing."

The small bird plunged into the lake and swam deep. He came up and climbed onto the bank to rest, brushing his breast against the mud. Then he flew away singing. The bird's wings, tail, back, and sides turned sky blue. But where he had touched the mud, his breast was brown.

Identifying Author's Purpose

1. The author wrote the myth mainly to

   Ⓐ persuade readers to feel sorry for gray animals.

   Ⓑ inform readers about how birds got their colors.

   Ⓒ describe the beauty of the blue sky.

   Ⓓ entertain readers with a story about how the bluebird got its color.

Interpreting Figurative Language

4. The phrase *does not break his word* means

   Ⓐ "always does what he promises."

   Ⓑ "never splits a word at the end of a sentence."

   Ⓒ "always says things he does not mean."

   Ⓓ "never stops speaking in the middle of a sentence."

Identifying Author's Purpose

2. You know your answer to question 1 is correct because the myth mainly

   Ⓐ contains many details that describe things.

   Ⓑ provides facts or tells readers how to do something.

   Ⓒ tells a story that is enjoyable to read.

   Ⓓ tries to convince readers of something.

Summarizing

5. What is the bird's main problem in the myth?

   Ⓐ The bird can't fly when he's wet.

   Ⓑ The bird wants to be blue like the sky.

   Ⓒ The bird is afraid to go into the lake.

   Ⓓ The bird can't sing well enough to please the Great Spirit.

Interpreting Figurative Language

3. In the myth, the water is compared to

   Ⓐ the blue sky.

   Ⓑ the color of the animals.

   Ⓒ mud.

   Ⓓ a rain cloud.

Summarizing

6. Which of these is the best summary of the myth?

   Ⓐ A gray bird fights with other birds because all the birds are gray.

   Ⓑ A gray bird wants to be blue, so he does what the Great Spirit asks and is given blue feathers.

   Ⓒ All the gray animals want to be blue, so a gray bird has to be clever to get the color he wants.

   Ⓓ A gray bird has to dip into the blue lake to get his new color.

Here is an article about the moon. Read the article.
Then do Numbers 7 through 12.

A Brighter Full Moon

Each month, the moon changes from new, when it is all dark, to a bright circle of a full moon. Then it grows dark again. The moon takes $29\frac{1}{2}$ days to complete this cycle. You can watch these changes every month.

Did you know that all full moons are not the same? Like a lamp that can be adjusted, the full moon changes its brightness. Some months, it is brighter, and other months it is dimmer. Also, the full moon is larger some months and smaller other months.

Full moons are largest when the moon is close to Earth. At its nearest point, the moon is 50 thousand kilometers closer. This happens because of the shape of the moon's path. The path of the moon around Earth is not a circle but is instead more egg-shaped. Also, Earth does not sit at the center of the moon's path. Earth is off to one side. That means that sometimes the moon moves closer to Earth as it travels around Earth, and sometimes it moves farther away. At its closest point, the moon looks $\frac{1}{10}$ larger than its usual size.

The full moon glows over the cloudy atmosphere of Earth, as seen from the space shuttle Columbia

When a full moon is closer to Earth, more sunlight bounces off the moon and reaches Earth. So the moon looks $\frac{1}{5}$ brighter. If you watch the moon each month, you may notice the brighter glow.

So sometimes you can see more moonlight reaching Earth and a larger full moon. This adds up to a special treat that is second to none!

Identifying Author's Purpose

7. What is the purpose of paragraph three?

Ⓐ to tell a story about the moon

Ⓑ to explain why the moon is sometimes close to Earth

Ⓒ to persuade readers to watch how the moon changes

Ⓓ to describe the beauty of the full moon

Interpreting Figurative Language

10. Comparing the moon to a lamp that can be adjusted helps you picture the

Ⓐ changing size of the moon.

Ⓑ way the moon makes light.

Ⓒ beauty of the full moon.

Ⓓ varying brightness of the moon.

Identifying Author's Purpose

8. The article was written mainly to

Ⓐ inform readers about how a full moon can change in size and brightness.

Ⓑ amuse readers with a story about the moon's changes.

Ⓒ persuade readers to watch the full moon more carefully.

Ⓓ describe the features of the moon's surface.

Summarizing

11. What is the article mostly about?

Ⓐ how the moon changes from dark to full and back

Ⓑ the way the moon moves around Earth

Ⓒ how the full moon can change in size and brightness

Ⓓ why scientists can't explain the change of the moon's size and brightness

Interpreting Figurative Language

9. What does the writer mean by *second to none*?

Ⓐ "happens twice each month"

Ⓑ "the second phase of the moon"

Ⓒ "better than everything"

Ⓓ "something few people have seen"

Summarizing

12. Which is the best summary of the article?

Ⓐ You can see the dark, new moon and the full moon every month.

Ⓑ The full moon looks larger and brighter when it is closest to Earth.

Ⓒ The moon can sometimes be 50 thousand kilometers closer to Earth than other times.

Ⓓ The path of the moon around Earth is not a circle.

Final Review

PART ONE: Read a Folktale

Here is a Chinese folktale. Read the folktale. Then do Numbers 1 through 12.

Fox Tricks Tiger

One night, a tiger wandered along a river. The tiger was the most powerful animal in the forest. He was large and kingly with black stripes on his yellow coat. The puff of white fur around his face just caught the moonlight.

The tiger was following a wooded path that many animals used. The tiger was hungry, so he was looking for any small animal that would be tasty enough to eat.

Suddenly, the tiger heard the sound of something nearby. With his sharp eyes, he spotted something moving up ahead. He slipped into the brush to hide until the "something" drew closer so that he could see what it was. He waited as patiently as a stone.

Tripping along the trail was a reddish fox. The fox approached close to the tiger, and the tiger leaped from the brush, grabbing at the fox with his sharp claws. The fox knew he could not outrun the tiger at such a close distance, so he yelled, "Don't even think of eating me! I am the King of Beasts. The emperor of heaven named me. He would punish you."

The tiger had doubts.

"You think I'm kidding," continued the fox. "Just follow me and I'll show you. Every animal we meet will run when they see me."

"I'll follow you," agreed the tiger. The two walked down the trail. Just as the fox had said, every animal that saw them ran off in a fright.

"Fox, you are the King of Beasts!" exclaimed the tiger. "I will not eat you." The tiger did not realize that the animals were not running from the fox.

Meanwhile, the trouble-making fox slipped off into the forest. He was smiling impishly about his trick.

Finding Main Idea

1. The folktale is mostly about

   Ⓐ the types of food a tiger eats.
   Ⓑ the life of a fox in the woods.
   Ⓒ the way a fox tricks a tiger.
   Ⓓ the tiger's good ears and eyes.

Recalling Facts and Details

2. What color fur was around the tiger's face?

   Ⓐ white
   Ⓑ yellow
   Ⓒ black
   Ⓓ red

Understanding Sequence

3. What happened right after the tiger hid in the bushes?

   Ⓐ The tiger heard a sound.
   Ⓑ The fox yelled.
   Ⓒ The tiger saw something moving on the path.
   Ⓓ The fox approached close to the tiger.

Recognizing Cause and Effect

4. Why does the fox decide not to run from the tiger?

   Ⓐ The fox is tired from running all night.
   Ⓑ The fox knows he is too close to the tiger to outrun him.
   Ⓒ The fox doesn't like to run along the river.
   Ⓓ The tiger is standing in the fox's way.

Comparing and Contrasting

5. In what way is the fox different from the tiger?

   Ⓐ The fox walks near the stream.
   Ⓑ The fox knows why the animals run when he and the tiger walk by.
   Ⓒ The fox scares animals but the tiger doesn't.
   Ⓓ The fox does not go out at night.

Making Predictions

6. What will probably happen if the fox walks through the forest alone?

   Ⓐ The animals will not run in fright.
   Ⓑ The fox will prove that the animals are afraid of him.
   Ⓒ The fox will have to run to keep up with the other animals.
   Ⓓ The fox will get lost in the dark forest.

Finding Word Meaning in Context

7. In the last sentence, the word *impishly* means

- Ⓐ "with sadness."
- Ⓑ "with pain."
- Ⓒ "in a mischievous way."
- Ⓓ "in a frightened way."

Identifying Author's Purpose

10. The main purpose of the folktale is to

- Ⓐ explain how tigers catch their prey.
- Ⓑ persuade readers that the fox is the King of Beasts.
- Ⓒ entertain readers with a story about a tiger and a fox.
- Ⓓ describe the beauty of a tiger.

Drawing Conclusions and Making Inferences

8. From the folktale, you can tell that the tiger

- Ⓐ does not like to eat foxes.
- Ⓑ is not a very good hunter.
- Ⓒ cannot see or hear things in the dark.
- Ⓓ does not know his own power.

Interpreting Figurative Language

11. The phrase *waited as patiently as a stone* suggests that the tiger

- Ⓐ was nervous about waiting.
- Ⓑ grew hard and cold.
- Ⓒ kept still as long as needed.
- Ⓓ looked gray.

Distinguishing Between Fact and Opinion

9. Which sentence from the folktale gives an opinion about the tiger?

- Ⓐ The tiger was following a wooded path.
- Ⓑ The tiger leaped from the brush, grabbing at the fox with his sharp claws.
- Ⓒ He was looking for any small animal that would be tasty enough to eat.
- Ⓓ The tiger was the most powerful animal in the forest.

Summarizing

12. What is the best summary of the folktale?

- Ⓐ A hungry tiger cannot hold onto his meal.
- Ⓑ To save his life, a clever fox tricks a hungry tiger.
- Ⓒ A tiger wanders the forest at night looking for food.
- Ⓓ A fox surprises a tiger and tells him a tall tale about the emperor of heaven.

PART TWO: Read an Article

Here is an article about CD's, or compact discs. Read the article.
Then do Numbers 13 through 24.

Everyone loves CD's. These flat, round plates hold music and other information. But do you know how music CD's are made?

A CD looks like shiny metal, but it is mostly plastic. The inside of a CD is a hard plastic disc. Over the plastic disc is a thin layer of metal. On top of the metal is a thin, clear plastic coating. The side of the CD without the label holds information for sound.

To make a CD, a singer records a tape, usually in a sound studio. As the singer performs a song, the sound is changed into electric signals. A special machine divides the signals into more than 44,000 parts, or bits, for each second the singer sings. These bits are recorded on the tape.

Next, the tape of the song is sent to a company that makes the CD's. The company makes a metal master disc. To do this, a machine takes the information from the tape and turns it into small bumps, or pits, in the disc's surface. The pits are so small that more than 1,000 would fit on the sharp end of a pin! This string of pits is called the track. The track moves from the center hole to the edge of the disc. The track is like a thin hair, except it is miles long.

The next step is to make metal copies of the master. The metal copies are the molds for making the CD's. Clear, melted plastic is forced onto the metal mold. This forms the inside of the CD. Next, the CD is coated thinly with metal. Finally, a machine sprays a thin layer of plastic on top of the metal for protection.

Finding Main Idea

13. The best title for this article is

Ⓐ "Listening to Your Favorite CD."
Ⓑ "Making a Master Disc."
Ⓒ "How a Music CD Is Made."
Ⓓ "The Many Uses of Plastic."

Recalling Facts and Details

14. The inside of a CD is a

Ⓐ thin metal layer.
Ⓑ clear plastic coating.
Ⓒ hard plastic disc.
Ⓓ special kind of tape.

Understanding Sequence

15. The boxes show three steps in making a CD.

The bits are recorded on tape.		The company makes a master disc.
1	2	3

Which step belongs in box 2?

Ⓐ The tape is sent to a company that makes CD's.
Ⓑ The singer performs the song.
Ⓒ The company makes metal copies of the master.
Ⓓ The CD's are molded out of plastic.

Recognizing Cause and Effect

16. The CD is coated with a thin layer of plastic

Ⓐ to hold the sound information.
Ⓑ to make the CD look better.
Ⓒ to protect the CD.
Ⓓ to change the sound to electric signals.

Comparing and Contrasting

17. What is one difference between the master disc and the metal copies made from it?

Ⓐ The master disc isn't for molding the plastic.
Ⓑ The master disc isn't metal.
Ⓒ The master disc doesn't have all the sound information.
Ⓓ The master disc is made last.

Making Predictions

18. Predict what would happen if some of the pits on a CD are damaged.

Ⓐ Some sound information would be lost.
Ⓑ The CD would play slower.
Ⓒ There would be no difference.
Ⓓ All of the sound information would be erased.

Finding Word Meaning in Context

19. In the article, what does the word *disc* mean?

  Ⓐ "a small target"
  Ⓑ "a round object"
  Ⓒ "a round plate that holds music"
  Ⓓ "a shiny piece of metal"

Identifying Author's Purpose

22. What is the author's main purpose for writing the article?

  Ⓐ to teach a lesson about CD's using an interesting story
  Ⓑ to persuade readers to buy CD's
  Ⓒ to describe uses of CD's
  Ⓓ to explain how a CD is made

Drawing Conclusions and Making Inferences

20. From the article, you can tell that making a CD of a singer's voice

  Ⓐ has several steps.
  Ⓑ can be done in a few seconds.
  Ⓒ is always completed in a studio.
  Ⓓ requires just plastic.

Interpreting Figurative Language

23. The track on a CD is compared to a hair because the track is

  Ⓐ thin.
  Ⓑ brittle.
  Ⓒ miles long.
  Ⓓ wavy.

Distinguishing Between Fact and Opinion

21. Which of these is an opinion?

  Ⓐ To make a CD, a singer records a tape.
  Ⓑ Everyone loves CD's.
  Ⓒ The singer performs a song.
  Ⓓ The sound is changed into electric signals.

Summarizing

24. What is the best summary of the article?

  Ⓐ A tape is used to make a master disc for a CD.
  Ⓑ A series of steps and several materials are needed to make a CD.
  Ⓒ A CD is made from a tape and has many layers.
  Ⓓ CD's are flat, round plates that hold music and other information.

PART THREE: Read a Biography

Here is a biography of Lhama Dhondup. He became the Dalai Lama, the religious and political leader of Tibet. Read the biography. Then do Numbers 25 through 36.

In 1935, Lhama Dhondup was born. He lived in a village in Tibet. As soon as he could talk, he told everyone that he was the new Dalai Lama. The Dalai Lama is the title given to the leader of Tibet. The title means "teacher whose wisdom is as great as the ocean."

When Lhama was just two years old, monks came to his home. They were looking for the next Dalai Lama. The boy saw the monks and exclaimed, "Now, I am going home!" The monks were not certain. But after they tested him, they led him and his family to a huge palace to live. In a ceremony, he was given his title, but he could not rule until he was fifteen.

The Dalai Lama studied subjects like all children in school. He also read about his religion. He had an interest in machines. He took the palace clocks apart and put them together again.

In 1950, he became the official ruler of Tibet. But China took control of his country. In 1954, he went to the ruler of China to make peace. But he did not succeed.

Five years later, the Chinese army invaded Tibet. The Dalai Lama fled to India. He crossed the icy mountains. Many of his people followed. Others stayed behind and suffered.

The Dalai Lama began traveling the world. He spoke for his country and for peace. In 1989, he received the Nobel Peace Prize. He said, "Because we all share this small planet Earth, we have to learn to live in harmony and peace with each other and with nature." This is the best advice anyone can give.

The Dalai Lama speaks in Santa Cruz, California, shortly after receiving the Nobel Peace prize.

Finding Main Idea

25. The biography mainly tells about

   Ⓐ the early life of Lhama Dhondup.

   Ⓑ a Nobel Peace Prize.

   Ⓒ problems between China and Tibet.

   Ⓓ the life of the Dalai Lama.

Recalling Facts and Details

26. According to the biography, the young Dali Lama was interested in

   Ⓐ school.

   Ⓑ machines.

   Ⓒ books.

   Ⓓ math.

Understanding Sequence

27. What did the Dalai Lama do after he became the official ruler?

   Ⓐ He became ruler of Tibet.

   Ⓑ He fled from the Chinese army.

   Ⓒ He traveled to China to ask for peace.

   Ⓓ He received the Nobel Peace Prize.

Recognizing Cause and Effect

28. Monks came to the home of Lhama Dhondup because they

   Ⓐ were looking for the next Dalai Lama.

   Ⓑ became lost.

   Ⓒ were running from the Chinese army.

   Ⓓ had been told the Dalai Lama lived there.

Comparing and Contrasting

29. One way the young Dalai Lama was like most children is that he

   Ⓐ took on an adult role at age fifteen.

   Ⓑ had a special title.

   Ⓒ lived in a great palace.

   Ⓓ studied school subjects.

Making Predictions

30. What did the Dalai Lama most likely do after 1989?

   Ⓐ return to Tibet under Chinese rule

   Ⓑ keep speaking for Tibet and for peace

   Ⓒ plan an attack on China

   Ⓓ criticize Tibetans who stayed in his country

Finding Word Meaning in Context

31. In paragraph five, the word *invaded* means

Ⓐ "enjoyed."
Ⓑ "attacked."
Ⓒ "left."
Ⓓ "avoided."

Identifying Author's Purpose

34. The biography was written mainly to

Ⓐ persuade readers to learn more about Tibet.
Ⓑ describe the places the Dalai Lama lived.
Ⓒ explain how the problems between China and Tibet began.
Ⓓ tell about the life of the Dalai Lama.

Drawing Conclusions and Making Inferences

32. Which one of these <u>cannot</u> be concluded from paragraph two?

Ⓐ The boy knew who he was.
Ⓑ The boy passed the test given by the monks.
Ⓒ The monks immediately knew the boy was the Dalai Lama.
Ⓓ The Dalai Lama lived in a palace.

Interpreting Figurative Language

35. The biography says that the title Dalai Lama means "teacher whose wisdom is as great as the ocean." This means that the Dalai Lama's wisdom is considered

Ⓐ wet and salty.
Ⓑ flowing and soft.
Ⓒ wonderful and vast.
Ⓓ wavy and strong.

Distinguishing Between Fact and Opinion

33. Which of these is an opinion?

Ⓐ He also read about his religion.
Ⓑ The Dalai Lama fled to India.
Ⓒ This is the best advice anyone can give.
Ⓓ He spoke for his country and for peace.

Summarizing

36. Which of these is the best summary of the biography?

Ⓐ The Dalai Lama won the Nobel Peace Prize.
Ⓑ The Dalai Lama was born for greatness and has worked for peace in Tibet and the world.
Ⓒ A war with China kept the Dalai Lama from ever ruling his own country.
Ⓓ In Tibet, a group of monks controls the country.

Acknowledgments

page 97: "Autumn Storm" is reprinted with permission of Barbara K. Mindell. Copyright 2002.

Illustration Credits

Leslie Alfred McGrath

Photography Credits

©Bettmann/CORBIS pages 11, 25, 60, 62, 67, 84, 114, and 122

Paul Dyer Photography pages 18, 61, 69, 102, and 119

www.arttoday.com pages 4, 6, 33, 74, 83, and 106

D.H.S. Sp.ED